Pearls: Natural, Cultured and Imitation

Butterworths Gem Books
Edited by Peter G. Read

Beryl
John Sinkankas

Garnet
John D. Rouse

Pearls: Natural, Cultured and Imitation
Alexander E. Farn

Quartz
Michael O'Donoghue

In preparation

Jet and amber
H. Muller and H. Franquet

Opals
P. J. Darragh

Topaz
D. B. Hoover

Butterworths Gem Books

Pearls: Natural, Cultured and Imitation

Alexander E. Farn

Butterworths
London Boston Durban Singapore Sydney Toronto Wellington

First published 1986

© Butterworth & Co (Publishers) Ltd. 1986

British Library Cataloguing in Publication Data

Farn, Alexander, E.
  Pearls: natural, cultured and imitation. –
  (Butterworths gem books)
  1. Pearls
  I. Title
  594′.11   SH375

  ISBN 0-408-01382-6

Library of Congress Cataloging in Publication Data

Farn, Alexander, E.
  Pearl, natural, cultured, and imitation.

  (Butterworths gem books)
  Bibliography: p.
  Includes index.
  1. Pearl industry and trade.   2. Pearls.
  I. Title.   II. Series.
  HD9678.P4F37   1986   338.3′71412   85-26906
  ISBN 0-408-01382-6

Photoset by Butterworths Litho Preparation Department
Printed and bound in England by The Garden City Press,
Letchworth, Herts

Preface

When asked why I had chosen the lengthy and very specific title of *Pearls: Natural, Cultured and Imitation* for this book, my reply was that it was because the lay public, and even people in the trade, use the term 'pearl' very loosely indeed. It is to be hoped that the book will clarify the distinctions between the varieties and make clear the point that the word 'pearl' must be applied only to natural pearls as found in oysters and mussels whose shells have a nacreous lining.

As a worker in the London Chamber of Commerce Laboratory, and later as the Director of this Laboratory which is responsible for the issuing of certificates of authenticity, the correct description and use of words, i.e. nomenclature, was an important part of my written work. My earlier rôle had been chiefly in testing loose calibré rubies, sapphires and emeralds, together with gemstones mounted in jewellery. These calibré stones totalled hundreds of thousands, and possibly topped a million, so that towards the end of my career I came to think of myself as a 'coloured-stone' gemmologist rather than as a pearl man.

An inherited task on becoming the Director of the Laboratory was to read gemmological writings and keep abreast of the activities of the outside world. In a prominent American journal's review of a museum's collection, the writer, whilst believing that the endoscope was obsolete, noted that the use of X-rays was the most reliable and satisfactory method for testing pearls. The reviewer added a personal *cri de coeur* for enlightenment on this method which was so often referred to but so seldom described. Consequently, I decided to write something of the methods and techniques founded and improved upon in our laboratory from the early days of 1925 until the present time.

Written by a professional laboratory worker employed to determine accurately the provenance of gemstones and pearls, this book will, I hope, explain some aspects of pearls, cultured pearls and their imitations. It is not intended for either the marine biologist or the zoologist, rather it is hoped that it will provide interest and useful information for both the trade and the public.

A. E. Farn
Frinton

Acknowledgements

When I decided to write about pearls many people took an interest, not least my late predecessor, colleague and friend, Basil Anderson. He sustained me with a wealth of literature and comments and a steady stream of notes, photocopies and letters, in addition to our normal correspondence. My wife typed and re-typed the entire contents and guided me grammatically along these tedious paths. Alan Jobbins read through the work and made many useful corrections to the presentation, as well as loaning and donating many colour transparencies of his own.

Certain portions were specially read through and I am grateful in this respect to Dr J. Nelson and Leslie Fisher for their expertise on X-ray apparatus. Professor K. Simkiss helped on nomenclature, as did the British Museum of Natural History's Department of Zoology. At the British Gem Testing Laboratory (known in the jewellery trade, particularly in London, as 'The Laboratory'), K. V. Scarratt and his staff were always helpful with photographs and discussion of pearl testing procedure and problems. I received tremendous help and enthusiasm from John Jerwood in Tokyo as well as from the Cultured Pearl Company in Hatton Garden. Boris Norman of the Australian Pearl Company supplied interesting photographs of the Australian scene as well as discussion on trade in general.

R. K. Mitchell provided several colour transparencies which required his special skills and patience. I am indebted to A. Kanai of the Japan Pearl Exporters Association and Katsuhiko Terekawa of Shiga Prefectural Pearl Cultivating Cooperatives for facts, figures and a book entitled *Pearls* by Dr Shohei Shirai. Koji Wada, National Research Institute of Aquaculture, Kashikojima, gave me lecture notes, together with papers he has written with K. Simkiss. Jean-Paul Poirot, Director of the Paris Laboratory, provided information in his *Éléments de Gemmologie* as well as having been professionally helpful in our mutual pearl problems. The pearl and precious stone trade section of the London Chamber of Commerce, under whose auspices The Laboratory has functioned in its several titles, permitted publication of pearl-testing figures which are themselves historical, being from the first-ever pearl-testing station in the world. If I have overlooked any name it is an inadvertent omission and not intentional. In general, I have mentally struggled with the task but enjoyed the necessity and compulsion so produced to maintain and renew acquaintance with the world which revolves around The Laboratory, Hatton Garden, and those places which were for me so enjoyable.

Contents

Chapter 1
Profile

As is well known, pearls are found in oysters and mussels. Nevertheless, the so-called 'oysters' are, in fact, closer to scallops than they are to the normal edible oyster.

Although pearls produced by oysters and mussels are a product of nature, it is not normal for an oyster to produce pearls; they result from an intrusion. L. J. Spencer, in his book *A Key to Precious Stones* (1946) says (on p 230) 'they are the result of a morbid condition of the mollusc', ...'the tomb of a parasitic worm is not really a pleasant object with which to bedeck a fair neck'.

The foregoing is a very brief and perhaps inelegant introduction to the subject of pearls and their origin, but before embarking upon the intriguing theme of the causes of pearls, it must be said that despite the somewhat off-putting vision conjured up by the words 'tomb' and 'parasitic', or even 'morbid condition', pearls in truth are beautiful as well as being extremely rare. 'Perfected by nature and requiring no art to enhance their beauty, pearls were naturally the earliest gems known to prehistoric man'. Such is the opening sentence of the monumental work *The Book of the Pearl* (1908) by George Frederick Kunz and Charles Hugh Stevenson.

The word 'pearl' should be employed only in reference to natural pearl, but many people unacquainted with the genuine article apply the word loosely to both the natural and the artificial varieties. Established pearl merchants and traders, and large numbers of internationally-represented jewellers and merchants, are combining under the auspices of CIBJO to control the correct description of gems, gemstones and allied materials. CIBJO stands for Confederation Internationale de la Bijouterie, Joaillerie, Orfevrerie, des Diamants, Perles et pierres, 1961. This is a body dedicated to co-ordinating efforts made for the promotion and protection of the trade in dealing between members of the trade themselves and in dealings with

1

the public. Four sectors representing manufacturing, wholesaling, stone dealing and retailing meet individually as necessary and report annually.

The Persian Gulf (Bahrain), the Gulf of Mannar, north western Sri Lanka, the northern and north western coasts of Australia, Tahiti, the Mergui Archipelago, the Sulu Sea, Venezuela, New Guinea, Borneo, the Gulf of California and Mexico are, among other areas, the chief sources of pearls and mother-of-pearl.

It is generally accepted that any mollusc (shellfish) which has a nacreous (mother-of-pearl) inner lining to its shell can, under suitable conditions, produce a pearl, albeit not necessarily a fine one. The vast majority of pearls fished are misshapen, or very small, or of poor colour; consequently, these do not enter the gem trade, and most poor-quality pearls are used as a 'medicine' said to have aphrodisiac properties.

For preference, pearls should be spherical, but they do occur as more irregular shapes which are known as 'baroque' (or 'barroks') and 'blister' pearls, and very small ones are referred to as 'seed' pearls. Spherical (cyst) pearls are usually found loose in the soft body tissue of the oyster, whereas blister pearls are commonly attached to the inner lining of the oyster's shell. The causes of the spherical pearl and the blister pearl have been the subject of interesting research which has been carried out over many years by experts in various countries.

Pearls which are spherical and of good colour, whether it be white, cream or rosée, rank on the scale of importance with diamonds, emeralds, rubies and sapphires, but while the gemstone most frequently seen in a good-class retail jeweller's window is diamond, fine natural pearl is probably the rarest seen.

Briefly, the chemical composition of pearl is 90 per cent calcium carbonate with equal proportions of water and organic matter (conchiolin). The structure of pearls is of a concentric and radial nature and in their structure pearls can be of either columnar calcite or thin overlapping platelets of aragonite, or both. Calcite and aragonite are both calcium carbonate but each has a different crystal system, i.e. trigonal and orthorhombic respectively. These substances (calcite, aragonite and conchiolin) are secreted by cells of the mantle which covers the soft body, viscera, gills and other internal parts of the oyster. The mantle is responsible for the secretions which form the outer shell, its mother-of-pearl lining and eventually pearls themselves which are mainly nacreous (aragonite).

Cross-sections of pearls commonly show no recognizable nucleus but the centre has a brownish discolouration which, when it appears in drilled pearls, is a very strong indication of natural origin. Seasonal growth rings may show as concentric layers but these are not the extremely fine structure lines of overlapping platelets of aragonite which are submicroscopic and not visible to the eye.

Specific gravity (SG) is a property studied in the determination of pearls and cultured pearls. Although soft gems with a measure of 3½ on Mohs' scale of hardness, pearls are, nevertheless, tough by virtue of their combined radial and concentric structure. The layers consist of submicroscopically-thin sheets of aragonite crystals all at right-angles to the plane of the layer and pointing radially from the centre. Persian Gulf pearls have an average SG of 2.71 (2.68 to 2.74), and the Sri Lankan variety are broadly similar, while those from Australian waters on the north and north western coasts are among the highest SG, ranging from 2.67 to 2.78.

The pearl oysters from Sri Lanka and the Persian Gulf average approximately 7.5 cm in diameter as against those from Australasian waters which are commonly 20 cm across and others from a larger species of up to 30 cm which weigh 5.5 kg. In these larger pearl oysters the mother-of-pearl value of the shell is greater than that of the pearls found.

Pearls can occur in shades of white, cream and rosée, depending upon their 'orient' and provenance; other factors which govern colour being conchiolin as a layer just below the surface, or a conchiolin-rich centre. Quality of orient depends upon the surface structure of the overlapping platelets (layers) of nacreous aragonite. The distance between these very, very fine ridges (which diffract light) and the reflection from these thin overlapping layers combine to give the subtle nuance of colour or colours termed the 'orient of the pearl'. Australian pearls are generally whiter and less lustrous but denser than any other pearls.

Pearl oysters are fished from 'paars' (the banks on which they live) comprising 'culch' (rock formations) to which young oysters attach themselves. They need a gentle flow of water with sufficient food and an equable temperature. Their natural enemies are starfish, borers and sponges; in addition, altered tidal currents and sea-bed movement can cause loss of food and a drop in temperature; and a shifting of sand can smother the oyster beds. Such occurrences can be catastrophic for pearl fishing. There are accounts of pearl fishing in Sri Lankan waters where once literally millions of oysters were fished in a season, giving fine yields of pearls, but later fishings saw relatively meagre results. Opinions have varied as to what causes these disasters – over-fishing, red tide, alteration of current flow, starfish predation, have all been mentioned as possible culprits.

Certainly, pearls are a rarity when one considers the life cycle of the pearl oyster and the dangers from its natural enemies. As well as these natural hazards the extra permutations of not only sheer survival but also the triggering-off of the pearl formation process by some chance and purely accidental intrusion of debris or parasite, or by internal injury, add more dimensions to the enormous odds against pearl formation. If, in addition, one considers the infrequency with which oysters produce, fine, coloured, sizeable, spherical pearls, it will be seen why fine natural pearls are the rarest of precious gems.

Throughout history pearls have formed an important part of the treasures of eastern potentates as well as those of European monarchs and dynasties. Their great value and rarity, as with other gems, has prompted imitators to attempt to produce a similar product. The imitation of pearls, however, has never caused the pearl merchant or jeweller much trouble in identification.

The opacity of pearls places a limitation upon the methods of investigation when the pearl merchant is faced not with the detection of imitation pearls but with that of cultivated or cultured pearls. The extremely clever use of the biological function of the captive pearl oyster to secrete a natural thin covering to a spherical bead nucleus almost destroyed the legitimate pearl market at the turn of the century.

The early attempts at pearl culture and the ultimate success make a fascinating story, and these activities together with the manufacture of instruments to detect cultured pearls, are themselves landmarks in the history of gems.

Summary of the composition, specific gravities and chief sources of pearls

Pearls occur in marine oysters, freshwater mussels and certain other molluscs, both bivalve and univalve. Generally speaking, jewellery-quality pearls consist mainly of calcium carbonate (in the form of aragonite), organic conchiolin and water. Basically, osyter and mussel pearls have a structure of overlapping microscopically-fine layers of aragonite crystals which, being perpendicular to the layers, are thus pointing radially from the centre of the pearl.

The broad bracket of specific-gravity (SG) value, particularly of Persian Gulf and Gulf of Mannar pearls, is derived from SG determinations taken on more than 1000 pearls at the London chamber of Commerce laboratory in the early days of intensive pearl research. These are as follows:

SG	under 2.70	2.70–2.72	2.72–2.74	Over 2.74
Oriental pearls: per cent	10	52	27	11

	CaCO$_3$	Pearl composition – %age values Conchiolin	H$_2$O
B. W. Anderson	92	4	4
Robert Webster	82–86	10–14	2–4
Walter Schuman	84–92	4–13	3–4
Kunz and Stevenson	91.72	5.94	2.34

Occurrences

Salt-water pearls (oysters)

Source	Colour/size	SG	Shell type
Persian Gulf (Kuwait-Bahrain)	Finest quality small	2.68–2.74	Bivalve
Gulf of Mannar (Sri Lanka)	Finest quality small	2.68–2.74	,,
Red Sea (Arabian shores)	White		,,
N/NW Australian coasts	Large, dense white	2.68–2.78	,,
South Seas islands	Usually large	Similar to Australia	,,
Venezuelan islands (Margarita and Cubagua)	Small translucent, glassy		,,
Mexican fisheries (Gulf of California) Mexico (Pacific coast)	Metallic hues, black		,,

Freshwater pearls (mussels)

Rivers and lakes ⎫	In general, pearls ⎫	
America ⎪	from mussels have ⎪	
Scotland ⎪	a much more subdued ⎪	
Saxony ⎪	orient than that ⎪	
Bavaria ⎬	of oyster pearls and ⎬	Bivalves
Sweden ⎪	are of less financial ⎪	
Russia ⎪	importance. ⎪	
France ⎪	Their SGs range ⎪	
China ⎭	from 2.66 to 2.78 ⎭	

Other pearl-bearing molluscs

Indian Ocean, giant clam (*Tridacna gigas*)	Large white, non-nacreous	2.81–2.87	Bivalve
West Indies/Florida coast, common conch (*Strombus gigas*)	Distinct pink, non-nacreous	2.81–2.87	Univalve
California, Japan, New Zealand, abalone clam (*Haliotidae*)	Brilliant hues – green, blue, yellow	Often with hollow centres	,,
Australian waters, pearly nautilus (*Nautilus pompilius*)	Yellow – not common		,,

Chapter 2

The origin of pearls

The origin of pearls is still a matter of interest and investigation. We know that broadly speaking they come from oysters and mussels. What we are not one hundred per cent sure of is what precisely it is that triggers the formation of pearls, since they are not the 'normal' product of an oyster but are the result of a morbid condition within the mollusc. The condition which causes pearl production, i.e. their origin, has been the subject of much surmise, discussion, research and theorizing.

The earliest-known writings on pearls are, of course, not as scientific as those of the later centuries. For hundreds of years much has been written in romantic/poetic vein, almost one might say in fairy-tale language. Traces of mumbo jumbo have lingered till the present day but fortunately, because of the pressures of science and the economic climate, research had to proceed and facts had to be ascertained. Even though discussion continues, we know now that certain conditions do arise which cause pearl formation, and those conditions will be fully described as we proceed.

It is necessary and of considerable interest, therefore, to read some accounts of early views on the origin of pearls. To this extent much of the following derives from certain extracts from Kunz and Stevenson's *The Book of the Pearl* which was written near the end of the first decade of this century and before the advent of the successful cultivation of spherical cultured pearls (*circa* 1920). It lacks only the later data of optical and X-ray beam methods of detection of cultured pearls and later non-nucleated cultured pearls. Other workers in mainly European countries devised accurate methods of detection and proof for natural and cultured pearls in the 1920s and onwards.

Such are the erudition and skills of the co-authors who provide a seemingly limitless bibliography and references, it seems pointless to write an individual article which must, of necessity, derive from reading *The Book of the Pearl*. Thus, the most cogent factual and chronological details of early workers, their findings and hypotheses are extracted and recorded in this account of the origin of pearls.

6

Later in this book we will deal with modern pearl production, marketing, uses and detection of artefacts.

Many theories on the origin of pearls have been put forward by naturalists in various countries, and as with all experts, it is possible to read each work and feel that its author is correct. With all workers and scientists, results become accurate as progress is made with more sophisticated equipment and methods. When one reads even a brief list of early eminent scientists' theories, it is fairly obvious that the grain-of-sand theory is not entirely displaced. The parasitic worm-intruder theory and the sac formation all merit consideration. Professor W. J. Dakin suggests on page 116 of his book *Pearls* (1913) that pearls are induced either by foreign bodies (sand grains, parasites or other objects) or by internal products of the pearl-producing mollusc. Raphaël Dubois presumed parasites as possible origins of pearls (1901 and 1903) and again, according to Dakin, states in a then recent summary: 'Il existe deux categories de margaritose ou maladie perlière; l'une parasitaire et l'autre non parasitaire.'

There is no lack of romance in connection with the origin of pearls, both in the fancies of the East, the traditions of the West or even in the sober science of today. To appreciate some of the vast amount of work done and research into the origin of pearls, the following table is produced from Dakin's account of the theories given or considered by various workers. It is interesting to note that the latest date given (1912) must have been close to the heyday of the pearl markets of the world, when prices of fine pearls were astoundingly high. Since at that time there were no cultured pearls upon the market, most research centred upon the pearl-producing oysters, the supplies and their continuity, the diseases and causes of poor crops from the pearl-oyster fishing grounds. The findings of scientists of that period on the structure of pearls, their chemical nature and possible origin, and the biological knowledge derived, helped both sides in the pearl and cultured-pearl confrontation which began around 1920 to 1925. Thus we see that although the preceding discussion upon cultured pearls may be a digression from the 'origin of pearls' saga, it serves to emphasize the stimulus of necessity provided by competition.

To revert, however, to the earlier works and theories by various authors, according to Professor Dakin, which follow:

Author	*Theory of cause*
Aelian	Flashes of lightning
Rondeletius (1554)	Parasites and concretions
Various 16th century writers	Eggs of the mollusc
Redi (1671)	Grains of sand
Réaumur (1717)	Solidification of shell-forming liquids
Home (1826)	A modified view of the egg theory, i.e. abortive ova.
Filippi (1852)	*Distomum,* a worm parasite
Kuchenmeister, von Hessling and Meckel } (1856)	Parasites, sand, eggs

Moebius (1857)	Entozoa
Kelaart (1857–1859)	Sand, diatoms, eggs and parasites
Garner (1863)	*Distomum,* parasites
Comba (1898)	Parasites
Dubois (1901, 1903)	Parasites
Jameson (1902)	Parasites
Herdman and Hornell (1902–06)	Parasites, etc
Seurat (1902)	Parasites
Giard (1903)	Parasites
Boutan (1904)	Parasites
Rubbel (1911)	Shell substance
Jameson (1912)	Shell repair substance and perhaps parasites

The origin of pearls has been the subject of much speculation among sages, scientists and naturalists of all ages. Needless to say, repetition of such opinions has perpetuated a considerable amount of misinformation and belief. The author's own practical experience in the hard-headed world of a Hatton Garden pearl-testing laboratory dealing mostly with pearl traders and merchants has, at times, been shaken by somewhat trite remarks such as 'pearls are tears'. Such remarks are uncommon; nevertheless, the impact it produces in a leading laboratory gives cause to consider how these easily-repeated and somewhat emotional phrases still persist among the fringe members of the trade.

Dew-formed pearls

The world of antique gems and jewellery attracts many part-time dealers. These uninformed people moving around the trade, auction rooms and 'antiques fairs' pick up a patter which, to the man in the street, sounds convincing. Quite possibly such phrases have their origins in quotations from literature of the playwrights and poets of early history. Kunz and Stevenson in *The Book of the Pearl* state (on p 37): 'With scarcely a single exception every recorded theory from the 1st century BC to the 15th century AD evidences a belief in dew-formed pearls'.

Poetry which gives such pleasure to its readers can readily be forgiven its choice of words or turn of phrase if in such manner it brings pleasure to the reader or listening audience. Poetry appeals to the emotions, whether by sonorous phrase or elegant description of beauty, whether it be '. . . ten thousand saw I at a glance – a host of golden daffodils', or '. . . full many a gem of purest ray serene'. Such words, being but a few among tens of thousands, serve to delight us – they linger long and latent in our memory. When used at some later date in a possible sales talk or even in a light-hearted discussion, they are given credence and perpetuate misinformation. Poetic licence is freely admitted and greatly treasured, whether it be by Sir Walter Scott, as in his *Bride of Tremain:*

The pearls that long have slept
These were tears by Naiads wept,

or as in one of Shakespeare's most lovely and consoling thoughts:

The liquid drops of tears you have shed
Shall come again, transform'd to orient pearl.

These and many more other quotations taken from Kunz and Stevenson's book serve to illustrate how repetition can give almost factual credit to an author's or poet's fantasy. For those who wish to browse and revel in a host of beautiful extracts from early writers, lovingly portrayed and classified, the section by Kunz and Stevenson on the origin of pearls provides a veritable feast. The section quotes freely and fully from many of the early writers and affords a fascinating view on the thinking of the more literate section of the world of that day. Of pearls they write: 'In luster they so closely resemble the limpid sparkling dew-drop as it first receives the sun's rays that the ancients very naturally conceived that pearls are formed from drops of dew or rain. The legend is that at certain seasons of the year the pearl oysters rise to the surface of the water in the morning and there open their shells and imbibe the dew-drops which in the course of time, aided by air and sunlight, are transformed into lustrous pearls. Pearls so formed can suffer in perfection of form, colour and luster if the air and sunlight are not received in sufficient quantities. Although this may seem to us to be remarkably absurd, it was the kind of belief repeated and repeated which was universally accepted for centuries by learned men in Europe as well as primitive peoples who delight in the mystical and fantastic.'

Quoting further extracts, it is difficult to realise fully how much the poetic attributes to the acknowledged chaste and subtle beauty of pearls and their origin has remained and been accepted as fact. William Camden (1551–1623), in whose honour the Camden Historical Society of England was named, accepted the theory of dew-formed pearls. He stated that the River Conway in Wales 'breeds a kind of shell, which being pregnated with dew, produce pearl'; and again, speaking of the River Irt in Cumberland he said: 'In this brook, the shell fish, eagerly sucking in the dew, conceive and bring forth pearls.'

What are more striking are the details of a letter then recently received (*circa* 1908) from the American Consul at Aden that this view was held even then by the Arabs of this region. Giving a reason for the current scarcity of pearls in the Red Sea, he stated: '. . . there is a belief among them that a pearl is formed from a drop of rain caught in the mouth of the pearl oyster which by some chemical process after a time turns into a pearl; and as there has been little rain in that region for several years there are few pearls.'

Certainly, repetition tends to harden people's beliefs, especially if authority is given to its perpetuation by a well-known or authoritative name, and particularly if he is a poet and not just a marine biologist.

Writing of the native Indians in one of the first books on America, the Italian historian Peter Martyr, in his *De Orbe Novo* (1517), stated: 'The perfect knowledge hereof is not to be looked for at the hands of these unlearned men who handle the matter but grossly and enquire no farther than occasion serveth'. Martyr was in fact commiserating with the Venezuelan Indians of Margarita Island on their non-acceptance or interest in the 'dew-formed' theory. A breath of fresh, albeit salt-laden air, is ventilated into the matter by the pungent observations of one of

England's great sea captains, Sir Richard Hawkins (1593), in *Voyage to the South Sea,* (p 133). He concludes that this must be 'Some old philosopher's conceit, for it cannot be made probable how the dew should come into the oyster.'

Queries and doubts

Gradually some writers were beginning to publish details of pearl oysters and pearls recovered from varying depths of water and of several pearls of dissimilar hue being fished from the same shell and querying the variations produced by the same dew.

In an abridged translation in Urbain Chauveton's edition of Girolamo Benzoni's *Historia del Mondo Nuovo* (1578), he refers to pearl oysters on the Venezuelan coast, as follows: 'Around the island of Cubaqua and elsewhere on the eastern coast are sandy places where the pearl oysters grow. They produce their eggs in very large quantity and likewise pearls at the same time, but it is necessary to have patience to let them grow and mature to perfection. They are soft at the beginning like the roe of fish, and as the mollusc gradually grows, they grow also and slowly harden. Persons who have seen them while fishing say that they are soft as long as they are in the sea and that the hardness comes to them only when they are out of the water.' Pliny the Second says as much, speaking of the Orientals, in Ch 35 of Book IX of his Historia Naturalia. 'But as to that author and Albert the Great and other writers upon the generation of pearls who said that oysters conceive them by means of the dew which they suck in, and that according as the dew is clear or cloudy the pearls also are translucent or dark, etc, *all this is a little difficult to believe* (present author's italics). Besides this, in many of the islands the Indians go fishing for them in ten or twelve fathoms depth, and in some cases they are so firmly attached to the rocks in the sea they can only be wrenched off by main strength. Would it not be difficult for them to inhale the quintessence of air there? It seems that it is the gem and the most noble part of the eggs of the oyster which are converted into pearls rather than any other thing; and the diversities of size, color and other qualities, proceed from the fact that some are more advanced than others, as we see eggs in the body of the hen.'

The egg theory

Thus the old theories of dew-formed pearls were beginning to be assailed. Despite this, as late as 1648 a medal struck in honour of Elena Piscopia of the Corraro family of Venice bore an engraved motto, 'Rore Divino' (by divine dew), and showed an open oyster shell receiving drops of dew.

That pearls were formed from the eggs of oysters became another theory between the 15th and 17th centuries. Writing of Henricus Arnoldi as an eyewitness, Christopher Sandius wrote in a letter dated 1 December 1673: 'Pearl shells in Norway do breed in sweet waters; their shells are like mussels but larger. The fish is like an oyster. It produces clusters of eggs. These, when ripe, are cast out and become like those that cast them, but sometimes it appears that one or two of these eggs stick to the side of the matrix and are not voided with the rest. These are fed by the oyster *against her will* (present author's italics) and they do grow, according to the length of time, into pearls of different bigness.'

This observation of the manner in which pearls are fed by the oyster 'against her will' leads towards a different school of thought on the origin of pearls. Probably because of the scarcity of pearl-bearing molluscs in Europe, naturalists were slow in appreciating their origin or devoting much time to studying them. Equally perhaps is the fact that the best specimens of pearls may well be found more prolifically in older, worn shells than the better-looking specimens appreciated by conchologists or collectors. Rondelet in 1554 propounded the idea that pearls are diseased concretions in the mollusca similar to the morbid calculi in the mammalia (gall stones?).

Structure similarities

The similarity in structural material or substance between pearl and the inner shell lining which produced it was first noted by Anselmus de Boot (*circa* 1600). That is to say, the similarity of mother-of-pearl to pearl. This observation is particularly interesting, its being so close to much current thinking. He states that pearls 'are generated in the body of the creature of the same humour of which the shell is formed – for whenever the little creature is ill and hath not strength enough to belch up or expel this humour which sticketh in the body, it becometh the rudiments of the pearl to which new humour, being added and assimilated into the same nature, begets a new skin, the continued addition of which generates a pearl.' A somewhat similar and succinct account is furnished by the Portuguese traveller, Pedro Teixeira (1608), who said: 'I hold it for certain that pearls are born of and formed of the very matter of the shell and nothing else. This is supported by the great resemblance of the pearl and the oyster shell in substance and color. Further, whatever oyster contains pearls has the flesh unsound and almost rotten in the parts where the pearls are produced, and those oysters which have no pearls are sound and clean fleshed.' (From *The Travels of Pedro Teixeira,* Hakluyt Society, p 180.)

Some hundred years after the observation by Teixeira, the famous French physicist, Réné A. F. de Réaumur, in *Mémoires de l'Académie des Sciences* (1717) pages 177–194, studied the cross-section of pearls by microscope and found them to be concentric layers, whereas the structure of shell (nacreous) lining was similar but curved. He suggested that pearls were misplaced pieces of organized shell formed by a secretion which overflows from the shell-making organ, or from a ruptured organ connected therewith. This rupture or overflow is ordinarily produced by the intrusion of some foreign or irritating substance.

The following lines attributed to Sir Edwin Arnold bring beautifully to mind this intimation by Réaumur of a possible 'origin of the pearl':

Know you, perchance, how that poor formless wretch
The Oyster, gems his shallow moonlit chalice
Where the shell irks him, or the sea sand frets,
He sheds this lovely lustre on his grief.

Intrusion theory

Other workers and thinkers, among them the Swedish naturalist Linnaeus, propounded the theory that pearl formation was caused by an intrusion into the soft body of mussels. Linnaeus in 1761 had some success in producing pearls by introducing into the mussel hard substances such as nacre and metal on a fine silver wire. It is said that he received the patent of nobility for his services to science. Mention is made of Linnaeus' method under 'The cultivation of pearls' in Chapter 6, page 66.   It can be seen that both Réaumur and Linnaeus subscribed to the idea of introducing hard substances to form the nuclei of baroque or blister pearls which are usually attached to the shell lining.

Rare sand-grain theory

With spherical pearls, which are cyst or sac pearls, the theory of a hard, intruded substance does not totally stand up to examination. Only in rare instances recorded by Professor Herdman and others have grains of sand been noted as nuclei of pearls. Pearls are the result of pathological secretions; the grain-of-sand generalization must be relegated to 'rare occurrence only' in terms of possible origin.

Early attempts to grow pearls

Linnaeus wrote in a manuscript dated 6 February 1761 that he possessed the art of impregnating mussels for pearl production and offered, for a suitable reward from the State, to publish the 'secret' for the public use and benefit. He was preceded by some centuries by the Chinese who had a small pearl industry at work in two villages near the city of Titsin in the northern part of the province of Che-kiang, a silk producing region (*see* Chapter 6, 'Cultured pearls').

The Linnaeus and Chinese pearls were usually of blister or baroque type and were the produce of mussels, i.e. freshwater molluscs. Sir Everard Home, in *Philosophical Transactions* (1826), Pt III, noted (on pp 338–341) that when split into halves pearls from freshwater mussels, as well as oriental pearls from marine oysters, would show a brillant cell in the centre equal in size to the ova of the same mollusc. From these observations he promoted his 'abortive ova' theory. A description of his work, taken from *The Book of the Pearl,* is as follows: 'A pearl is formed upon the external surface of an ovum which, having been blighted, does not pass with the others into the oviduct, but remains attached to its pedicle in the ovarium, and in the following season receives a coat of nacre at the same time that the internal surface of the shell receives its annual supply. This conclusion is verified by some pearls being spherical, others having a pyramidal form from the pedicle having received a coat of nacre as well as the ovum.'

These conclusions of the grain-of-sand theory (pathological secretions formed by intrusion of hard substances, encystation of ova, etc) were accepted at that time and remained so until 1852.

Filippo de Filippi of Turin, whose work accords with that of Home, Linnaeus and Réaumur in respect of an irritating stimulus to pearl production, differs from them in identification of the nature of the irritant. He published his paper (*see* References) on the origin of pearls in 1852. Whilst examining the freshwater mussel *Anodonta cygnea* from ponds near Turin, he found that pearly formations, i.e. concretions, as well as trematode and parasitic worms, were present. The parasitic worm, which he named *Distomum duplicatum,* is found to be closely related to the parasite which causes 'rot' or distemper in sheep. He found, by microscopic examination of the smallest pearls, an organic nuclei which appeared to be the remnants of trematode. In other *Anodonta* mussels taken from regions not infested with *Distomum,* Filippi seldom found pearls. He stated that an important cause, not necessarily the principal one, of pearl formation in the mussels, was the parasite *Distomum duplicatum,* and others. Later he added *Atax ypsilophorus* as being a member of parasitic agencies which could excite secretions for pearl production. These he compared with the action of parasitic infection and formation of plant galls.

In succeeding years other workers, namely Friedrich Kuchenmeister in 1856 and Karl Mobius in 1857, included pearl oysters with pearl mussels in the actions or infections of parasitic agencies causing pearl forming secretions in Indian and American molluscs.

A further extension or development by Dr E. F. Kelaart, a medical officer in Sri Lanka, and his assistant Humbert, in 1859 revealed the important relation which Vermean parasites bear to the origin of pearls in Sri Lankan oysters. Kelaart and Humbert found that as well as filaria and cercaria, three other parasitical worms attacked the viscera and other parts of the pearl oyster, and both agreed that the worms played an important part in the formation of pearls. In the ovaries Kelaart also found eggs coated with nacre and forming pearls. He also propounded a theory that siliceous internal skeletons of microscopic diatoms could possibly penetrate the mantle of the oyster and so become the nuclei of pearls. His death a few months later ended these investigations.

Robert Garner, in the *Journal of the Linnean Society* (1873), Vol XI (pp 426–428), gave the presence of distomid larvae in the common English mussel *Mytilus edulis* as the agency for pearl formation in these mussels. Alfred Ciard and other French zoologists also found similar facts extant in other bivalves. Professor Raphaël Dubois, in *Comptes Rendus de l'Académie des Sciences* (1901), Vol 133 (pp 603–605), agreed the findings of Garner; he found that edible mussels on the French coast which contained pearls were infested with a parasitic larvae which he termed *Distomum margaritarum.* He equally boldly announced that, 'La plus belle perle n'est donc, en definitive, que le brilliant sarcophage d'un ver.' ('The most beautiful pearl is only the brilliant sarcophagus of a worm.')

The accent on parasites

Emphasis now, it seems, is upon parasitic invasion of the mussel and the oyster to promote secretions of pearl-forming materials. In Volume I of the *Proceedings of the Zoological Society of London* (1902), Professor H. L. Jameson wrote (on pages

140–166) of the relationship which exists between pearls found in English mussels *Mytilus* and the larvae of *Distomum somateriae*. 'This trematode worm has an interesting life history; it is found in three consecutive hosts, starting with a duck, the common scoter, followed by the tapes clam or perhaps by the common cockle and finally the edible mussel in which the second larval stage of the parasite stimulates pearl formation.' Jameson claimed to have produced small pearls at both Brighton aquarium and the fish hatchery at Kiel by infecting healthy mussels by associating them with infested molluscs.

Calco-spheritic structures

Jameson's paper in 1902 describes the trematode entering *Mytilus edulis* as a tailless cercaria often between the mantle and the shell; the larval worm later enters the connective tissue of the mantle where it assumes a spherical form. Both are visible to the naked eye, being approximately half a millimetre in diameter. At first, the worm occupies only a space lined by connective tissue fibrils, but soon the tissues of the host give rise to an epithelial layer which lines the space and ultimately becomes the pearl sac or cyst. If the trematode later completes its maximum term of life it dies and the tissues of the body break down to form a structureless mass which, owing to the rigid cuticle, retains the form of the parasite. In this mass arises one or more centres of calcification and the precipitation of carbonate of lime goes on until the whole larva is converted into a nodule with calco-spheritic structure. The granular matter surrounding the worm, if present, also undergoes calcification. The epithelium of the sac then begins to shed a cuticle of conchiolin, and from this point the growth of the pearl probably takes place on the same lines and at the same rate as the thickening of the shell.

Just as interesting and truly remarkable are claims made by Dubois who, in 1903, experimented with a pearl oyster *Margaritifera vulgaris* from the Gulf of Gabes on the coast of Tunis. In that area there was a great scarcity of pearls, namely, over a thousand shells yielding perhaps only one pearl. Oysters from Gabes were taken to the coast of France and associated with trematode-infested mussels, *Mytilus gallo-provincialis*. After a short period they became so infested that every three oysters produced an average of two pearls.

Jameson, in an examination of the cestode theory of pearl production (published in 1912 by the Zoological Society of London) reported his findings on the structure of the shell and pearls of the Sri Lankan pearl oyster, *Margaritifera vulgaris,* and an examination of the cestode theory of pearl production, is critical of the work of Professor Herdman who, at the invitation of the colonial government, in 1903 went to examine the pearl oyster resources of Sri Lanka, accompanied by his assistant, James Hornell (appointed in 1904 by the Ceylon Government as Marine Biologist, later adding the administrative duties of Inspector of Pearl Banks). Although Jameson had originally subscribed to the parasitic intrusion as a basis for pearl formation, he makes some hard allusions to the paucity and findings of Herdman. Such is the power of experts, we find ourselves reading and following their theories and accepting them because of the importance of their proponents' standing.

Perhaps some differences of opinion by various experts may be attributed to some early work being concentrated on mussel pearls which, in general, have a larger nuclei than those of Sri Lankan oyster pearls.

Sand grains and parasites

Nuclei are the basis of pearl formation; the various theories upon nuclei and their introduction remain the subject around which 'the origin of pearls' discussion revolves. It seems that there is not one basic cause for the formation of pearls but several. The grain-of-sand theory can be quoted as an extremely rare case indeed. Parasitic intrusions must be another and self-generated inclusion of the shell-making material of the oyster yet another. Herdman considered that in the Sri Lankan pearl oyster, several worms existing as parasites and thus stimulating peral formations, were cestodes, trematodes and nematodes, of which he prefers the larval cestode of the *Tetrarhynchus* form as the important cause. In 1905 his assistant, the previously-mentioned James Hornell, stated that the origin of pearls from *placuna* oysters from Tablegram Lake near Trincomali, north east Sri Lanka was due to minute larvae of the same species as that which causes pearls in the Gulf of Mannar oysters. Hornell stated that the living worm does not induce pearl formation but only after death of the larva in certain parts of the oyster, pearls being more numerous in oysters long affected. The life cycle is bounded by pearl oyster – trigger fish – fish-easting rays – pearl oyster.

Morphological change

Probably the most important cause of the origin of pearls is that of the parasitic intrusion, lending substance to the statement by Dubois that 'the most beautiful pearl is only the brilliant sarcophagus of a worm.'

In most animal bodies a cyst forms around intrusive wandering larvae. Fortunately such morphological change in the case of the pearl oyster results in something beautiful reflecting the character of the inner shell lining and even surpassing it in beauty. The examination of pearls by microscopic often reveals no visible nucleus and it is safe to say that the finest pearls are sac or cyst pearls. Certainly large intrusions into pearl oysters which become trapped between the mantle and inner shell lining are sometimes very radpidly covered with a thin transparent nacreous layer before decomposition takes place and remain as a permanent fascinating example of the nacreous secreting powers of the pearl oyster and pearl mussel. In the opening Profile of this book it was said that pearls are the result of a morbid state within the mollusc and the tomb of a parasitic worm.

When an irritant object enters its shell, the oyster tries to eject it, but failing this it isolates the intruder either by immuring it against the inner shell wall, thus forming a blister, or by encystation, i.e. in a sac, or cyst. Usually, the intruder is a parasitic worm which causes a depression on the surface of the mantle, slowly sinking in until it is in a hollow below the surface. Eventually, the hollow is sealed over, the parasite dies, and its skeletal remains receive a coating of conchiolin which hardens to form a nucleus. From then on, secreted fluids from the epithelial cells of the sac cover the nucleus with overlapping fine films of nacreous aragonite. If the oyster can move freely, the nucleus receives concentric layers which form that finest of pearls, a spherical cyst pearl. We now have a pearl of radial and concentric structure, chiefly of aragonite crystals radiating outwards from the centre. Movement restricted in any particular direction produces a variety of shapes such as oval, drop-shape or button-shape. A nacre layer laid flat would resemble a honeycomb structure of aragonite rhombs grouped in a pseudo-hexagonal manner, cemented by conchiolin.

In the second edition of his *A Key to Precious Stones* (1946), L. J. Spencer deals succinctly (on pages 229–231) with the whole pearl and cultured pearl problem in less than two pages. He manages to pack in, in pithy sentences, a concise condensation in which he states: 'Since pearls are the result of a morbid condition of the mollusc, it is possible to stimulate their formation and growth by artificial means. The result is the same, and it matters little whether the source of irritation has been accidentally swallowed by the oyster itself, poked in by a mischievous boy, or skilfully introduced by an ingenious Jap.'

Chapter 3

The history of pearls

Pearls are produced by molluscs with a nacreous lining, usually from warm Eastern waters. Today, the term 'oriental pearl' signifies natural pearl from oysters of Sri Lanka, the Persian Gulf and the Red Sea. These fisheries are the oldest known sea fisheries whilst those of China are from freshwater sources. Pearls were known to ancient man long before they assumed importance as jewels. Probably tribes living on the Indian coast fishing for food would eat the flesh of shellfish and discard any pearls discovered. The aborigines of Australia, as recently as 1867, were gathering oysters for food at low tide and probably appreciating the shell rather than any pearls.

To return, however, to the history of pearls, it was not until man developed and began to appreciate beauty that pearls and mother-of-pearl assumed an importance. Their importance in decoration, and later their value as barter, placed pearls in a venerated position. The sources of the Indian Ocean supplied the Indians with pearls and pearl shell. Centuries before Christ, in ancient sacred books known as the Vedas of the brahmans, records of decoration with pearls are found. An amulet decorated with pearls and mother-of-pearl is said to ensure long life and prosperity to disciples of Brahma. Certainly pearls assumed many virtues in the eyes of man, and perhaps an understandable virtue accredited to them was that of purity, a reflection of their symmetrical lines and color.

Pearls have a ready beauty unlike other gemstones which have to be mined, cut and polished. Edwin W. Streeter, when writing in his book *Pearls and Pearling Life* (1886) about the high estimation in which pearls were held by the Indians, Persians, Greeks and Arabs, describes pearls (on p 21) as 'these unostentatious little globules which have played a part in the progress of the world and civilization'.

There are records of pearls in ancient writings on clay artefacts unearthed in Persia which date the knowledge of pearls to several centuries BC.

Although pearls were part of ancient Indian commerce and luxury, there is no description of actual pearl fisheries in early manuscripts until the 2nd century AD when Mannar is mentioned as 'where pearls are found'. The Gulf of Mannar is, of course, now well known to gemmologists as a source of pearls.

The oldest surviving pearl ornament is in the Persian Gallery of the Louvre Museum, Paris. It is a three-row necklace of 216 pearls, discovered at Susa, the site of the winter palace of the Persian kings; it was found in a bronze sarcophagus by J. de Morgan in 1901. Knowledge of pearls and pearl ornaments may well have been lost to man by reason of the frangible nature of the literature, i.e. broken clay tablets, etc. It seems certain that pearls were depicted in ancient Persian sculptures as early as the 7th and 9th centuries BC.

Joan Younger Dickinson describes in *The Book of Pearls* (1968) the cult of shell and pearl worship and gives details of the three-row pearl necklace discovered at Susa. It is at least as early as the 4th century BC, and, she states, is a necklace built round the number three, a prime number, indivisible. There are three rows of pearls, 72 pearls per row, divided into nine equal sections by ten sets of three gold dividers. Each strand of 72 pearls represents two numbers which total nine, as do the three numbers in the group total of 216 which itself is divisible by three. The accent seems to be on the number three which to the Persians is symbolically sacred, as it is in the Christian Trinity, three being a male number, a fertility symbol numbering the parts of the male phallus.

Pliny the Second in his *Historia Naturalia*, stated in the 1st century AD that pearls were ranked first in the order of value among precious things and that the pearls worn by Cleopatra at the banquet she gave to Marc Antony were valued at 60 m sestertii. This value was equal to 1 875 000 ounces of silver. Kunz and Stevenson suggest in *The Book of the Pearl* (1908) that it was probably worth more in Roman times than at their time of writing.

Pearls which originated in early days from the Persian Gulf, Sri Lanka, India and the Red Sea found their way by barter or by conquest to other nations of the world. It seemed that then, as now 'oriental' pearls were the most important. Dakin states on page 4 of *Pearls:* 'It is often said that the presence of pearls in the molluscs of the rivers of the British Islands played some part in bringing Julius Caesar to our shores'. Some items of Roman or Greek jewellery incorporating or comprised entirely of pearls are still in existence in museums such as the Louvre (Paris), the British Museum (London) and the Metropolitan Museum (New York), to name but a few. A bronze statuette of Aphrodite, known as the 'Tyszkiewicz bronze' and said to be the most beautiful bronze Venus known, was acquired in 1900 by the Boston Museum of Fine Arts. It still has a pearl suspended from each ear on a gold wire. The statue's age is variously estimated as 500–430 BC, 400–336 BC or 330–146 BC, but the pearls are in a fairly good state of preservation.

The Chinese are recorded as having accepted pearls as payment or for tax purposes as long ago as 2000 BC. They were probably freshwater pearls.

The Chinese, Persians, Indians and Greeks all had a great love for and appreciation of pearls. Men, as well as women, wore pearls as signs of importance or badges of rank. Interesting accounts of such princes, emperors and moguls can be read in Kunz and Stevenson's *The Book of the Pearl,* as well as in Streeter's *Pearls and Pearling Life.*

References are made to Kubla Khan, Alexander the Great and Cleopatra by the chroniclers of those times, among whom were Marco Polo, Pliny, Homer and Tavernier. They depict the triumphs and tribulations, victories and defeats, the sacking and pillaging of the cities of Alexandria, Rome, Babylon and Constantinople. There are rich accounts of the exotic wealth of empires, their decline and fall, the increasing value and importance attached to pearls in the ancient history and pageantry of the East and to the later history of pearls in Europe, the Americas and Australia. Compilation of a comprehensive history of pearls would in itself be a monumental task – here we can only briefly touch upon the historical aspects in a book which primarily deals with the pearls themselves.

The name 'pearl' is variously attributed to Teutonic and Latin derivation. The Teutonic derivation is said to come from the diminutive of *beere,* a berry. Latin derivations are *pirula,* the diminutive of *pirium,* a sphere, and *pirula,* a pear – a common shape for pearls. The Romans gave the Greek word *margarita* to pearls but generally described them as *unio* when they were large and perfect. The word *margarita* was used to describe something of unique value, a cherished possession or a favourite child.

Following the sacking of Rome, Constantinople became the most important centre for wealth, art, and especially pearls, because of its control on trade. As time went by and man 'progressed', further pillaging continued in Europe. Towns of Gaul such as Toulouse and Narbonne were literally treasure houses furnished from conquests and pillaging. Carcassonne was reputed to hold magnificent items from Rome, including jewels from the sacking of the temple in Jerusalem in 70 AD. In turn, other cities were pillaged, Toulouse by Clovis and, in similar manner, Barcelona and Toledo churches were sacked by the Franks. A great appreciation of and demand for jewellery grew on the continent of Europe to the extent that a most skilful jeweller in the court of King Dagobert (628–638 AD) was made a saint – Saint Eloi – one of the most popular of saints in Gaul.

The production of important and imposing pieces of regalia, notably pearl-set crowns and covers of manuscripts, became a fetish. Among the jewels which were set in the covers of many finely-bound books pearls were of great importance. Unique tomes such as the missal at the library of Rouen took 30 years of labour, and the cover of the Ashburnham manuscript of the Four Gospels, which dates from about 896–899 AD, has set in its covers 98 pearls probably all of which came from freshwater sources in Europe.

In the 10th and 11th centuries AD most freshwater pearls were recovered from the rivers of Scotland, France and Ireland, and the Romans obtained many from England. Although the effect of returning Crusaders carrying jewels and pearls caused an appreciation in the monetary value of such jewels, pearls were not extensively used for ornamentation in England before the 12th century. Pearls had a certain importance as a medicine for many types of ailment; mostly small misshapen pearls were used as powders.

Before the 12th century, pearls were far more popular in jewellery in Europe than in England. On that Continent various sumptuary laws limiting private expenditure obtained, with the hope of quelling the demand and greed for pearls. A number of pecularly biased laws of possession were passed which affected the ownership and inheritance of pearls but many of these laws were carefully avoided, if not evaded. Simpler tastes and the improvement of cutting, faceting and polishing of crystalline gem material had some detrimental impact upon the demand for pearls which was further lessened by the discovery of diamonds in Brazil in 1725.

The supply of pearls from the Red Sea and Ceylon (now Sri Lanka) was not steady and the largest reliable supplies still came from the Persian Gulf. These factors, together with cheap imitations, saw for a time the decline of the pearl in Europe. The East, however, has always had, and continues to hold, a great regard and veneration for pearls. The Sri Lankan pearl fisheries, which had been lying dormant for 30 years prior to British possession in 1796, had several good seasons of output, followed by exhaustion. The South Seas islands, the Tuamotu Archipelago, and the Pacific coast of Mexico, together with the new sources in Australia (1861) and the vast supplies of freshwater pearls from the Mississippi in America, combined with the later development of diving apparatus, gave further boosts to the pearl industry.

Pearls have survived various setbacks, some fisheries becoming exhausted by over-fishing, some depleted by events such as changing tides and loss of food for the oysters. The pearl trade, which centred in later years on Bombay, London, New York and Paris, was affected in the early part of this century (1910–1925) by a decline in supplies, not a lack in demand. The advent of the cultured pearl, *circa* 1921–1925, caused a momentary slowing in the handling of natural pearls on the legitimate world markets, but this, as is shown in other chapters, was overcome. Earlier examinations of the oyster banks of Sri Lanka, in attempts to save these important fisheries, saw several comprehensive investigations by learned scientists (not always in agreement).

However, considerable strides were made in elucidating the origin of pearls. This knowledge, plus earlier findings, enabled the Japanese workers, led chiefly by Kokichi Mikimoto, to insert nuclei successfully into oysters and to produce spherical cultured pearls. The same knowledge, garnered with international co-operation, was used in like manner by scientists and skilled craftsmen to devise optical and X-ray methods to combat the threat of the cultured pearl. When all seemed settled and the laboratories which followed London's leads were happy in their ability to determine accurately, speedily and safely, natural pearls from cultured pearls, the Japanese, once again, showed their remarkable skill and aptitude by producing pearls without a nucleus from freshwater mussels in Lake Biwa, Japan. This remarkable achievement of producing cultured pearls from *mussels* in far greater amounts *pro rata* than from oysters has now gone the inevitable one step further with the production of non-nucleated cultured pearls from sea-water *oysters*. It is rather like the arms race, where one country produces new weaponry only to face another country's effective countermeasures. Just as strong fluorescence and distinct phosphorescence were useful weapons in the determination of freshwater origin, now we have the sea-water version from oysters, with no luminescent characteristics to aid us.

The turn of this century and its early years were tremendous years for natural-pearl production. The markets of London, Paris, New York and Bombay were handling record totals of pearls, for which astronomical prices were paid. An excellent and very readable account of the then pearl fishing of oyster banks, paars and culch, is given by B. W. Anderson in his book *Gemstones for Everyman* (1976), a book written for gemmologists and non-gemmologists to understand and enjoy without too much resource to purely scientific data. Anderson, by virtue of his role as Director of the world's first laboratory set up as pearl-testing stations by the London Chamber of Commerce, had a wealth of experience gained by having metaphorically 'cut his teeth' on pearls. Without deviating too far from this present history of pearls by embarking on an enthusiastic review of *Gemstones for Everyman,* the section on pearls is extremely readable and entertaining – here you have first-hand accounts of the London pearl market of the early 1920s.

The 'Bombay bunches' (Plate 1) strung and finished by fine silver wire tassels are seldom fashioned nowadays except by request. Many modern-day craftsmen do not have experience in assembling the bunches and today, the main purchasers of pearls in Bombay are Arabs who prefer made-up jewellery such as necklaces rather than loose drilled pearls. Some idea of the value of pearls can be obtained from a quoted item for a single pearl fished off the coast of Broome, Western Australia, which weighed 103 grains (25 carats) and in June 1938 was priced at £10 000 trade price. (*News Chronicle,* London). When inflation is taken into account, the sum of £10 000 in 1938 would assume almost astronomical proportions today.

Chapter 4

The structure and anatomy of the pearl oyster

Before proceeding to describe the structure and anatomy of the pearl oyster, some clarification was thought desirable upon some of the names employed in the description of sources and the type of oyster, mussel and/or other pearl-producing molluscs.

The two line drawings (*Figures 4.1* and *4.3*) are taken from page 28 of Dakin's *Pearls* (1913) and page 6 of William Reed's booklet *Huîtres Perlières de Polynesie*

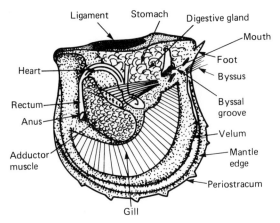

Figure 4.1 Mantle and gills of the Sri Lankan pearl oyster (after Herdman)

(1973). These serve to indicate the main parts of the anatomy. Dakin has referred to *Margaritifera vulgaris*, which is nowadays termed *Pinctada radiata*. The drawing from William Reed is probably based upon *Pinctada margaritifera* which is extensively fished around the islands of Polynesia (*See Figure 4.3*, p 27).

Because of the changes in nomenclature noted when referring to older text books compared with more modern usage, it was decided to request clarification on certain of the species' names. The list which follows is not a complete list of pearl-producing molluscs but it represents some of the most frequently used or referred to species. The details are replies to enquiries and were furnished by the Curator of Molluscs from the Department of Zoology, British Museum (Natural History). It was pointed out that there was a shortage of sufficiently well considered monographs on shells to provide unequivocal answers to specific questions. Thus, the following reads as a series of replies to questions:

(1) *Pinctada maxima* (Jameson, 1901)
(2) *Pinctada margaritifera* (Linnaeus, 1758)
(3) *Pinctada carchariarum* (Jameson, 1901)
(4) *Pinctada albina* (Lamarck, 1819)
   All of the above pearl oysters are recorded from Australia. Numbers (3) and (4) are the same variety. *P. maxima* and *P. albina* are possibly limited in their distribution in the tropical south-west Pacific (Philippines to western and northern Australia). (2) *Pinctada margaritifera* (Linnaeus, 1758) is widely distributed from the Red Sea throughout the tropical Indo-Pacific. The variety name '*erythraeensis*' (Jameson, 1901) is unnecessary as it is the same as *Margaritifera sensu stricto*.
(5) *Pinctada mazatlanica* (Hanley, 1856) is probably the valid name for the species of the 'Panamanian' faunal province of American authors, i.e. Baja California/Gulf of California, southwards to Peru.
(6) *Trochus niloticus* (Linnaeus, 1767) is widely distributed throughout the tropical Indo-Pacific, and is collected along the Queensland coast for button-making and nuclei for cultured pearls.
   Pinna nobilis (Linnaeus, 1758) is the valid name for the Mediterranean (East Atlantic) species.
   Pinna seminuda (Lamarck 1819) occurs in the West Atlantic and may be a synonym for *Atrina rigida* (Lightfoot, 1786).
(7) *Pteria penguin* (Röding) the 'Black-winged pearl oyster', is widely distributed throughout the Indo-Pacific from the Red Sea to northern Australia and southern Japan.
(8) *Placuna placenta* (Linnaeus, 1758) is not a 'true oyster', but belongs to the super family *Anomiacea* (family *Anomiidae*) commonly called 'jingle shells' or 'saddle oysters'.
(9) *Haliotis tubercalata* (Linnaeus, 1758) is the valid name for the European (Channel Islands) species.
(10) The Pearly Nautilus (*Nautilus pompilius*) (Linnaeus, 1758) belongs to the class *Cephalopoda*, sub-class: *Nautiloidea*, order: *Nautilida*. The term '*Tetrabranchiata*' was formerly used as a sub-class but has been revised.
(11) Freshwater pearls in Britain (and Europe) may come from the freshwater pearl mussel which is validly named *Margaritifera margaritifera* (Linnaeus, 1758).
(12) The Chinese freshwater pearl mussel is more likely to be *Cristaria plicata* (Leach, 1814).
   Anodonta cygnea (Linnaeus, 1758) is the European 'Swan mussel' and is not known to occur in China.

Other authorities

A monograph by a French author, G. Ranson, on the genera *Pinctada* (*P.*) is
mentioned by another source in reply to a query upon the term *P. fucata*.
Confusion has existed among workers mixing *P. martensi* with *P. radiata* (and
referring to it as '*P. fucata*'.)

P. martensi and *P. radiata* are separate species. The new authority is quoted as
saying that *P. fucata* is not a valid species and should not be used.

The Sri Lankan pearl oyster is similar in structure and size to that from the
Persian Gulf, i.e. approximately 9 cm across; they have been the most prolific
sources of pearls and are quoted as type examples. Other areas such as north west
Australia, Venezuela, Pacific Ocean islands, Gulf of Mexico, etc, also provide
pearl oysters.

The pearl oyster is closer in relationship to the scallop than to our edible oyster.
It is termed a 'bivalve mollusc', 'bivalve' meaning two halves or shells and 'mollusc'
indicating a soft-bodied animal protected by a hard exterior shell covering. The
group name for such bivalves is *Lamellibranchiata,* and it includes edible oyster,
the edible mussel, cockle and almost all other marine animals which produce
pearls. The scientific name refers to the characteristic plate-like gills. The soft body
of the oyster is enclosed between the two valves which are hinged together along a
dorsal line in relation to the body. The opposite ends of the valves are ventral and
the valves are thus symmetrically and laterally disposed upon the soft body, namely
a left valve and a right valve. Although the valve has a rounded outline the hinge or
dorsal end is flattened and finished as wings or auricles (*see* wing pearls, p 53). The
shell is not thick (as it is in mother-of-pearl oysters from Australia) but it is lined
with brilliant and iridescent nacre. The external surface is rough, dull and usually
encrusted with other organisms growing on it. Some authors state that rough waves
and rocky sea beds cause a thick protective outer shell layer as a natural defence,
whereas oysters from sheltered positions on smooth sea beds have a thinner shell
offering less defence.

The shell layers

The shells of the oyster (*Figure 4.2*) and freshwater mussel are composed of three
main layers, and a fourth occurs where the adductors muscles (closing muscles) are
attached (*see* 'Muscle pearls' in the Glossary).

The outer horny layer, termed the 'periostracum', is secreted by the cells of the
edge of the mantle and does not increase in thickness once it is formed. The other
layers increase in thickness with age and hence in young oysters the outer layer is
thicker in relation to the other layers than it is in adult oysters, due to wear and
rubbing having taken place.

The periostracum is sometimes continued in the form of numerous *lamellae* into
the next layer which is thicker than the outer layer and termed the 'prismatic layer'

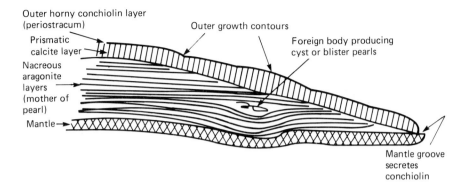

Cross-section of oyster shell and mantle

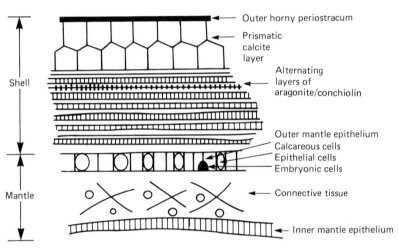

Figure 4.2 Growth layers of shell, cross-section of shell and mantle (after J.-P. Poirot)

because it is composed of columnar crystalline calcite. Again, this layer is secreted by the edges of the mantle and does not increase in thickness once it is formed.

The third innermost layer is the most important of all; it is the nacreous (mother-of-pearl) lining which continues to grow and thicken throughout its life and is secreted by the entire surface of the mantle. The nacreous layers are composed of aragonite (the labile form of calcium carbonate), and they consist of microscopically-thin platelets overlapping each other parallel to the surface of the shell but with zig-zag edges which can just be seen using a 10× lens. The edges and filmlike layers together combine to give the exclusive 'orient of pearl' optical effect due to interference and diffraction effects. There is a parallel between the structures of mother-of-pearl and pearls.

The fourth layer is termed the 'hypostracum'. This consists of layers of columnar calcite crystals at right-angles to the surface of the shell, and it is found between the muscle and the shell.

Shell growth

The shell grows at the edges. Growth of the periostracum (outer protective layer) and the prismatic layer is controlled by secretions from cells at the edge of the mantle. The mantle, being a flap of tissue which covers the soft body parts of the oyster on each side (valve), it follows precisely the individual shape of the shell walls (which in fact it formed). The mantle, or pallium, is usually thickened at the edges in bivalves and here its colour is darker than the interior part. The mantle is formed of connective tissues with numerous blood spaces – it has an extensive colourless blood supply. The edge of the mantle secrets the two layers, the periostracum and the prismatic, and can renew them only at the margin but does not thicken them.

   The inner nacreous layer is secreted by the whole surface of the mantle (the epithelium) and continues to grow in thickness during the life span of the oyster. The wonderful part of the oyster-shell story is that certain parts of the mantle secrete normally the periostracum layers, and the nacreous layer is secreted by the entire surface of the mantle. When an oyster shell suffers damage the shell is repaired by the epithelial cell sections of the mantle (nacreous) in the order of the periostracum prismatic and mother-of-pearl. This is an important parallel with growth of the pearl proper.

Shell formation

Shell formation, which is by simple organs, or organs which appear simple, is in fact very complicated. The formation is due in its entirety to the cells, sometimes termed the 'epithelial cells', which cover the mantle. These cells manufacture a mixture of organic and inorganic substances, namely, conchiolin and calcium carbonate ($CaCO_3$). The crystallization of the calcium carbonate takes place outside the soft-bodied oyster (surrounded by its mantle of thick skin) and thus forms the hard shell cover. This process produces three layers: a waterproof conchiolin protection and two inner layers of calcium carbonate in different physical forms as trigonal calcite and orthorhombic aragonite.

   All the cells seem practically similar but what kind of governing conditions exist to regulate this organic and inorganic production is not known. This production of comparatively hard shells of varying shapes with delicate markings, by an apparently simple cell in a soft tissue, is truly a wonder of nature.

The soft body

Considerable force is required to prise open an oyster, due to the resistance offered by the adductor muscle which serves to close the shell. The tough elastic ligament assists in the opening of the oyster. It is in fact the hinge joining the two shells. *Figure 4.3* shows the basic parts of the soft body of one of the oyster shells.

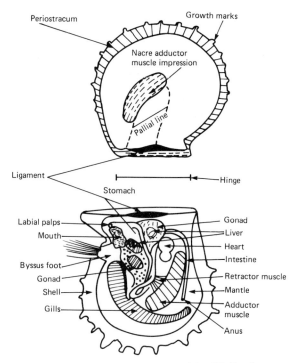

Figure 4.3 Anatomy of the pearl oyster (after W. Reed)

The foot

In the area between the adductor muscle and the dorsal hinge is the soft body which contains the heart and the viscera. Ventral to the adductor muscle are the flat and plate-like gills, which suspend in the cavity between the two valves.

The foot, to be found in the visceral mass just below the mouth, is extremely muscular and is capable of marked expansion and contraction. This alteration in size is due to cavities which communicate with the blood system, and when dilated with blood the foot becomes several times larger than its contracted size. It is the expansion and contraction of the foot which gives locomotion to the oyster in the manner of the snail.

However, additional to this movement is the action of the secretion by byssus fibres which attach the animal to rocks. The fibres issue from a gland in a pit on the ventral side of the foot; from this runs a groove to another pit at the other end of the foot. Applying the foot to a rock presses the edges of the byssal groove together to form a tube through which pass the secretions from the byssal gland. The secretions harden in sea-water and in a few minutes the foot contracts and withdraws leaving the oyster attached to the rock by a series of fine byssus fibres. When an oyster or mussel is pulled by force from its anchorage it breaks from that surface and not from the byssus gland. After a period of time the fibres are renewed by fresh secretions.

Muscles

In addition to the adductor muscle, there are six other muscles connected with the foot, and these additional muscles are termed 'retractors' and 'levators'. The retractors are found in the walls of the byssus gland, one to each shell, and the levators are two posteriors and two anteriors. By contracting these muscles the foot is either moved sideways or retracted.

The pallial cavity

When a pearl oyster is opened the gap between the internal faces of the mantle flaps is simply a space. This is termed the 'pallial cavity', and here the sea water enters and flows over the gills which hang down from the adductor muscle. The gills are not the only respiratory organs. The mantle lobes also, which contain numerous blood spaces in extremely thin-walled cavities, allow the interchange of gases. The plate-like gills, of which there are two, occur as two double plates of half gills, i.e. two half gills to each side of the body.

Breathing and feeding

All living organisms must breathe and the gill plates, which perform the same function as do the lungs in mammals, extract oxygen from the sea water and pass out carbon dioxide from the process of respiration. For the system to be effective it is necessary for water to flow over the gills, i.e. there must be a flow or current movement, and the gill plates achieve this in an interesting manner. The plates are composed of a number of filaments hanging side-by-side which are joined by delicate hair-like processes, giving an appearance of a firm, sickle-shaped plate. A touch of the finger would separate the filaments, so that the gill plate resembles a comb with soft pliable teeth kept in position by adhering to each other. They could be likened to the delicate structure of a feather. The gills are covered with these delicate microscopic hair-like processes, sometimes termed 'cilia', in a regular and definite pattern, and it is the continual wafting of the cilia which causes a faint current in the water,

As an example of the cilia effect, consider a field of corn of a fairly even height standing high and ripe all over the field. Light winds blowing across the corn crop moves it with a wave-like rippling motion that reveals the sweep of the air current. If this effect is imagined in reverse, the cilia effect is seen. A self-generated movement of corn stalks would cause an air current; similarly, the cilia moves and this starts up a wave motion which in its turn sets the water in motion. Water entering the shell between the two mantle lobes passes over and through the gill plates. Passing through the gill plates continually, the water loses some of its oxygen and leaves the shell at the posterior exhalant opening.

Food particles entering with the water of the inflowing current are swept anteriorly along the gill margins until they reach the flaps known as 'palps', a pair of which is found at each side of the body. The outermost pair is a prolongation of the upper lip of the mouth and the innermost is a prolongation of the lower lip, and the groove between each pair leads to the mouth.

The palps, like the gills, are covered with cilia so that the food particles are wafted along to the mouth by the wave motion. Particles accepted as food pass into the alimentary canal, otherwise they are rejected. Those rejected are picked up by a current of water running with and close to the margin of the mantle and carried back until the exhalant opening is reached where they exit together with the waste water that has passed through the gills. In similar manner, cockles, mussels and other bivalves obtain their nutriment.

The blood system

Because the blood of molluscs is practically colourless, it is not commonly realized that bivalves have a heart and a system of blood vessels. The function of the blood does not differ greatly from that of red blood, since other chemicals present replace the red haemoglobin which is essential in the human respiratory system. The system is much simpler than it is in man, since only pure blood flows and in only one direction.

The heart is centred dorsally as a single ventricle, a muscular walled bag, on each side of which is an auricle with thinner walls. The muscular contraction of the ventricle is rhythmic, each contraction forcing blood out through two arteries into the system. This heart-beat effect is part of the one-way system. After its contraction the ventricle is dilated by blood sucked from the auricles. Valves prevent blood re-entering the auricles when the ventricle contracts. The gills and mantle supply the auricles with pure blood only.

The excretory organs

To deal with waste matter the pearl oyster has simple tubes which perform the same function as kidneys do in mammals. Excreted matter is removed from the blood circulating in the walls of the tubes into the cell lumen, and also from the walls of the heart into the pericardium, eventually reaching the exterior.

The nervous system

The pearl oyster and mussel do not actively search for food but are sluggish in their simple gaping in slight currents of water to extract any food which may be trapped by the cilia movement. Since their 'struggle' for existence is of such a passive nature, it is only to be expected that they have very simple nervous and sense organs.

It is not possible to point to the 'head' of an oyster, it does not exist. Its sense organs cannot be compared with those of higher animals (the vertebrates); the oyster simply uses them for orientating itself and for testing the water which must flow constantly throguh its shell. In place of eyes there are light-sensitive areas at the edges of the mantle such that a shadow thrown across the area causes the positive closure of the shell. This sole means of defence at the edges of the mantle is found in the area where it serves its purpose best – not necessarily the area where one might expect the brain to be.

The nervous system is simple, consisting of three ganglia (nerve-cell aggregations) connected by nerve fibres. The cerebral group is found in the 'head' region, and the pedal ganglia which are connected to the cerebral ganglia form a mass at the base of the foot of the oyster. The third pair of ganglia is found on the adductor muscle. Each valve has its system. Sensory fibres (from the periphery of the oyster body) and gills transmit nerve impulses to ganglian cells and thus to muscles causing reflex action. A difference in the temperature or content of the water, or a shadow across the mantle edge, is sufficient to cause the transmission of a nerve impulse. At best it is a very low sensory system.

The reproductive system

In the studies of pearls, whether they be on the study of origin, structure, chemical composition or provenance, there are certain common-sense fundamentals which are so obvious as to be almost not quite worth mentioning. Without oysters, or for that matter mussels, there would be no pearls, which brings us back to the fact that the rich harvests and poor harvests of pearls depend upon the oysters which in their turn need ideal conditions on their paars (the banks on which they live) with the right amount of culch (rocky anchorage at the right depth), plus freedom from their predators (the starfish, borers, sponges, rays, etc). Basic to all these needs, of course, is the reproductive system.

The only form of defence enjoyed by the harmless rabbit is its reproduction capability. In like manner, such is the gregarious habit of the oyster, the chances of its sperm meeting an egg are fairly certain. In oysters the sexes are separate, unlike the scallop which it closely resembles, but to the eye all oysters appear similar.

Determination of the sex of an oyster necessitates a close examination of the repoductive organs. These organs consist of multitudinous branched tubules covering the digestive gland, intestines and stomach. The eggs of spermatozoa are formed inside little sacs in the tubules which join into each other to form ducts which further merge into a large duct on each side of the opening to the exterior. Upon maturity, eggs and/or spermatozoa are ejected into the sea in which the oyster has its being. Thanks to the very large numbers which develop and to the closely-packed formations of hundreds of thousands of oysters in a comparatively small space, there are good chances of a meeting between sperm and egg, by the fusion of which the act of fertilization is accomplished.

This haphazard method of reproduction is encountered wherever tremendous tolls are imposed by environmental hazards. Thus does nature wisely provide, to produce, protect and maintain a balance, not of pearls but of oysters. The pearls which may eventually be formed are themselves the result of a morbid condition within the mollusc, representing a further extension of the rarity factor in the production of a single pearl. If all the eggs produced by oysters were successfully fertilized, the end result would be mounds of oysters rising like islands from the seas.

The phylum mollusca

The term 'mollusc' covers a wide range of soft-bodied and usually hard-shelled animals. The mollusca comprise one of the major subdivisions or phylla of the animal kingdom. The molluscs which are of most importance to the gemmologist, pearl merchant and jeweller, are oysters, mussels, clams and snails which usually possess nacreous-lined shells and can produce pearls.

The phylum mollusca is the second largest of the animal kingdom, containing as it does some 128 000 living and 35 000 fossil species. To this enormous abundance must be attributed the popularity of shell collecting since such a wealth of diverse shells exists, all waiting to be gathered. The distinguishing characteristics of molluscs are the adaptation of the ventral surface of the body as a muscular foot for locomotion and the modification of the integument (the mantle) for the secretion of a protective calcareous shell.

Chapter 5

Sources of natural pearls

The Persian Gulf

Encircled by Iran, Kuwait, Saudi Arabia, Qatar and the United Arab Emirates, the Persian Gulf (*Figure 5.1*) is roughly 600 miles long by 100 miles wide, and the Strait of Hormuz at its southern end connects it to the Gulf of Oman which opens out into the Arabian Sea. For over 2000 years the Gulf has been a valuable source of fine pearls.

Undoubtedly, oil exploitation has altered the life style of the poorest sections of the communities in this area. Where once divers and crews keenly sought employment in pearling, today that labour force can find more regular and better pay in the oil industry. Equally, the unhappy state of affairs resulting from war and accident has seen considerable oil spillage and subsequent pollution of the area. It remains to be seen whether or not the damage caused to marine life will accumulate and become permanent and sound the death knell of pearl fishing in the Gulf.

Although there has been a falling-off in pearl production since some of the better-authenticated records were published, rich Arabs still show a strong continuing interest in pearls. In recent years the author has noted the strong pattern of trade in London where large stocks of pearls have been held since before the Second World War. There was an ever-increasing demand for fully-documented natural pearls of important sizes by pearl merchants with a largely Arab clientele. This reviving interest earned a report in the trade paper, *The Retail Jeweller,* under the heading of 'Back to the Persian Gulf'.

Before the coming of the oil wealth of Iran, most of the financing of pearl fishing, i.e. for supplies, boat crews, etc, was undertaken by Hindus. Both Arabs and Hindus have a continuing appreciation of pearls. The maritime tribes of Husa and Oman were the chief workers in the pearling fleets, but due to the repressive conditions of the financiers, many divers inherited their fathers' debts and had little chance of earning a reasonable return for their labours.

32

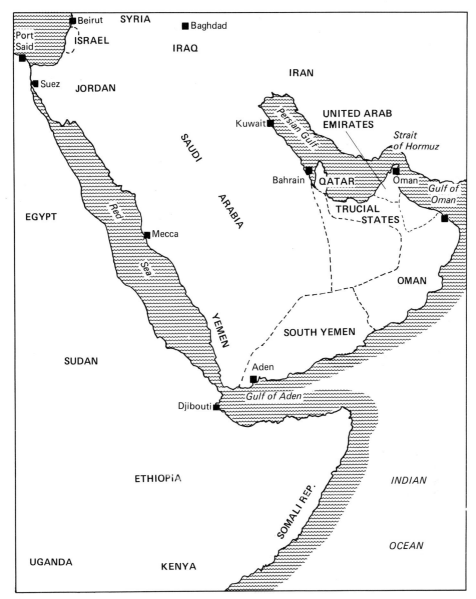

Figure 5.1 The pearl-producing areas of the Persian Gulf and the Red Sea

The oyster reefs are most abundant upon the Arabian side of the Gulf with the Bahrain islands being the centre of the pearl-fishing industry. The largest island of the group is itself named Bahrain.

The oyster reefs, which are distributed prolifically over level areas of rock and coral growth, are found at depths varying from 12 to 100 ft. However, Persian Gulf divers seldom plunge deeper than 70 ft whereas their Arab counterparts in the Red Sea were noted for their ability and prowess in reaching depths of 150 ft.

The destination of most of the area's pearl production is still Bombay where the pearls are drilled, graded and strung. They used to be sold strung by size on silk and in tasselled bunches very attractively bound with silver wire. These were known as 'Bombay bunches'; today such bunches are produced in this manner only by special request.

Another aspect of change in the Gulf pattern is that mentioned by B. W. Anderson on page 525 of his 1983 revision of Webster's *Gems: Their Sources, Descriptions and Identification* regarding non-nucleated pearls being produced on Kish Island in the Persian Gulf. Not too long ago, such was the authority of the rulers of the areas that severe punishment was dealt out to anyone found in possession of cultured pearls.

The Gulf has had a chequered history. It was known to the Romans and 'Tylos' was their name for Bahrain. In the 16th century the Portuguese took over the main ports and were noted for their heavy taxes on the pearl-fishing industry for over 100 years. At Hormuz in the strait during the period of the Portuguese occupation, the treasures of the Orient were gathered to such an extent that it was considered to be the jewel of the centre of the world, that 'world' being represented by a ring in which the jewel was Hormuz. Today it comprises a collection of some hundred or so huts. The fisheries were taken in the early 17th century by the Persians who promptly lowered the taxes on boat licences.

The fisheries are operated all the year round compared to those of Mannar which are of a shorter period. Diving is restricted to shallower waters during April and May, the deeper waters then being too cold. The period of June to September is one of great activity in the Gulf when provisioning, buying, selling and general preparations are made for the pearling season.

The oyster which is common to both the Persian Gulf and the Gulf of Mannar is *Pinctada radiata,* formerly described as *Pinctada vulgaris.*

Although piracy had been a way of life in the past for some of the maritime tribes, the influence of British gun-boats persuaded them that pearl fishing was a preferred occupation. However, the reduction in the sizes of the various pearl-fishing fleets, as reflected in comparison with authentic records, is significant. In the early 1900s the Persian Gulf fisheries employed 3500 boats of all sizes, with 1200 of the better boats sailing from Bahrain. In the period between the two World Wars the size of the fishing fleet diminished to about 600 vessels, and post Second World War, following the development of the oil industry in the area, there have been further inroads into the pearl-fishing fleet.

Crews were composed mainly of Arab divers, the rope and safety workers usually being drawn from the Bedouin or Persians.

Since the early records were made, little has been recorded in the way of change in the method employed for gathering the oysters. The general method is still that of nude diving. When the dhows arrive at the fishing grounds the broad square-bladed oars which they carry are set out at right angles to the sides of the boat to serve as steadying devices and also as bollards for the divers' ropes. For each diver there are two ropes; one has attached to it a heavy stone of about 50 lb in weight and has a loop for the diver's foot when he is descending; the second rope is attached to a string bag which the diver either carries in his hand or slings around his neck. This bag is for holding any oysters which he may gather, and its rope is for hauling the diver back to the surface.

Prior to descending the divers put on leather finger stalls to protect their fingers whilst plucking the oysters from the coral reefs or rocks, and fix leather clips to their noses.

Divers do not 'dive' in the normal sense, they go feet first, standing on the stone weight, which allows them to step off on reaching the sea-bed. There they gather as many oysters as they can in the short space of time during which their lungs can function without fresh air. The alertness and assiduity of the rope 'minders' left in the boat is tremendously important for the divers' safety. A sharp tug on the rope signals to the minders to haul them up as fast as possible, since most divers stay till the end of their limit. The divers also speed their ascent, when possible, by hauling themselves up the ascending rope.

Although the method of payment by advances by rather hard-headed employers was somewhat ameliorated by Shaik Hamad bin Isa al Khalifah in 1923, the lot of the pearl diver continues to a very hard one.

The Red Sea

An important source of pearls was the Red Sea, together with the Gulf of Aden which is its opening into the Indian Ocean, but the area's importance and products were overshadowed because of its proximity to the Persian Gulf. Today, as in the case of most of the once-famed sources of pearls, the output from the Red Sea is much diminished.

The principal species of oyster which was fished in this area was *Pinctada margaritifera erythraeensis,* four to five inches across, similar to that of the Persian Gulf, found singly and not occurring in banks. It was fished chiefly for its mother-of-pearl and the occasional pearls found were welcomed as an additional profit. The mother-of-pearl shell is carved in Bethlehem and Jerusalem and, like the Polynesian shell, is a popular product for the tourist industry.

Earlier writers also mention *Tridacna gigas,* the huge clam capable of trapping a diver by his hand or foot. The Pinna shell is also mentioned as a source of small, brown/reddish-coloured pearls.

The Arab divers (nude) of the Red Sea were said to be capable of descending to greater depths than the divers of the Persian Gulf.

Fishing in the Red Sea in the more prolific days was done from dhows and small vessels known as 'sambuks'. The first fishing season starts in March and finishes at the end of May, followed by a second period in the autumn during September and October. Arab ownership of dhows and financing by Hindus, with Bombay as the eventual destination of the pearls, left little reward for the divers and fisherman. Sometimes, due to the length of the fishing period and advance payments to the crews' families, the unfortunate workers would find themselves in debt at the end of a fishing season. When one considers the short working life of a diver, due to the occupational stresses imposed upon his constitution and the very real possibility of death or wounding by sharks, and other hazards, it is small wonder that the products from the Red Sea oyster are nowadays very meagre.

The Gulf of Mannar (India)

The sea area known as the Gulf of Mannar (*Figure 5.2*) is bounded on its western side by the southern tip of India and on its eastern side by the large island of Sri Lanka, formerly Ceylon. An isthmus protruding from each country towards the other forms an almost unbroken land boundary to the north of the Gulf.

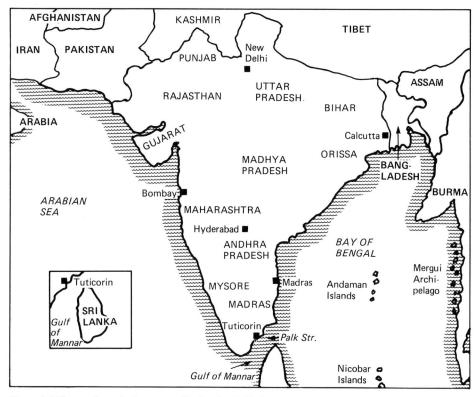

Figure 5.2 The pearl-producing areas of India, the Gulf of Mannar and Sri Lanka

There is no absolute record of the beginning of the pearl-fishing trade in this Gulf, but it probably began well over 2000 years ago. The writings of the early travellers, Arabs, Greeks and Romans, furnish details in their respective histories of travel. The pearl fisheries of the Gulf are noted for the quality of their products which have an excellent lustre and orient, and undoubtedly the fisheries conducted in earlier times were instrumental in attracting foreign merchants to the area.

When the Portuguese arrived in southern India around the middle of the 16th century they Christianized and afforded protection to the local population of Paravas against the threat of the Mohammedans who were becoming proficient divers. The Paravas had enjoyed near-monopolistic rights due to their tribute payments to the monarch of the time. The Portuguese also assumed control of the fishing. In 1658 the Dutch took over from the Portuguese until, in 1796, control passed to Great Britain. This situation lasted until Great Britain relinquished her role over India in 1947, since when pearl fishing has become a State monopoly.

The fishing rights, taxes, protection, changing rulers, as well as continual change in harvest and lack of continuity, are all part and parcel of the history of the Indian pearl banks of the Gulf of Mannar.

Herdman and Hornell, among others, had reported upon the condition of the pearl fisheries relating to the banks, the paars, and the diseases. Their reports shed light upon the reasons for the apparently irregular chronological periods of pearl fishing.

The banks, or paars, upon which the oysters breed and feed are rocky outcrops of which there are about eighty on the Indian coast of the Gulf of Mannar. Twenty-six fisheries were held in the 156 years following that of 1805 when over 7 000 000 oysters were fished. The paars appear to be formed from calcareous materials discharged from three rivers and cemented together by the action of polyzoa and millipores. This applies to the Sri Lankan coast as well as to the Indian side of the Gulf. The paars which are further from the shores suffer less from silting by mud and sand effluents than do those closer to the coast. Mud is considered deadly to the oysters.

The Indian paars vary in size from 0.5 km^2 to 25 km^2 and their depths below the surface vary from the inshore series of 12–14 metres (39–46 ft) to the outer series of 18–25 metres (59–82 ft). One of the largest banks/paars is just off the Madras coast at Tuticorin.

The paars are inspected by a method of regular rectangular partitioning in which regular dives are made to bring up flora and fauna; the formation and condition of the sea bed are also noted, i.e. whether rocky, silted, coralline, etc. The numbers of old and young oysters are noted, and by means of carefully-graduated mathematical proportioning an estimate of the oyster population can be deduced. Provided that a certain percentage of the oyster is above a particular size, the paar is considered fishable, but even then a sample fishing takes place which decides the value of pearls taken from lots of one thousand oysters. The value level is decided by pearl merchants and if it seems probable that the fishery will provide adequate revenue to the Government, a pearl fishing will take place.

One of the most important features of the survey of paars and surrounding waters is 'spat fall', i.e. the crop of young oysters. Very often this is quite promising but sometimes the promise is completely wiped out by drifting sands or attacks by parasites. Sometimes a strong tide or current will sweep away the still-young oysters. They also have to contend with their natural enemies such as starfish, borers, rays, etc. Rays play an important part in the cycle of parasitic intrusion and infestation of the oyster which causes pearl formation; this seems a bizarre example of nature's handiwork.

When one considers the hazards of tides, temperatures, winds, currents, disease and predators, together with the peculiar cycle of parasitic infestation, plus haphazard fertilization and many other permutations of chance, the arrival of a perfectly spherical umblemished pearl of cream rosée hue is a near miracle. Beauty and rarity are attributes recognized by the prices paid for the queen of gems.

There has been considerable variation in the nomenclature of oysters. Genera names such as *Meleagrina pteria* and *Pinctada* will be found in use, but the oyster fished in the Gulf of Mannar is *P. radiata*, formerly described as *P. vulgaris*.

In a brief address entitled 'Pearls of the seas and oceans' given before the
Canadian Association in 1982 and reported in *The Canadian Gemmologist* pp 7–13,
D. S. M. Field discussed nomenclature. In the resumé by D. S. M. Field is the
promise of further work to be built upon this extremely useful description of the
sources of pearls.

The life span of the oysters on the paars in the Gulf of Mannar is reckoned to be
six years. They are sexually-mature at twelve months and spawn twice a year quite
prolifically in March/April and September/October. These are the periods in which
the weather is calm, i.e. before the monsoons, and when the temperature and
salinity of the water are high.

Gulf of Mannar (Sri Lanka)

Similar conditions of paars and oysters exist on the Sri Lankan side of the Gulf of
Mannar where the chief port for pearl fishing is a temporary settlement which
springs up at Marichchukkaddi, in the north west of the island. It is temporary
because, like the Indian paars in the Gulf, the Sri Lankan paars suffer the same
vagaries of production due to the tidal flow, silting, predators, etc.

Like the Indian fisheries, these came under British rule in 1796; and again
government reports were made of the state of the paars. The paars are reported to
cover an aggregate area of 50 miles in length by 20 miles in width in a wide, shallow
plateau off the north west of the island. They are situated between five and twenty
miles from the shore and the depths are given as five to ten fathoms (30–60 ft).

In the 1796 and 1797 fisheries tremendous crops were harvested due to the pearl
banks having been left undisturbed for a considerable period. The vicissitudes
caused by the conditions of drifting sands and strong tides sweeping away young
spat resulted in such concern at the depleted paars in 1866 that consideration was
given to the importation from the Persian Gulf of oysters for seeding, the oysters
being similar. From then on the results were haphazard, ranging from lean to glut
proportions. In 1905 in 47 working days between February 20 and April 21 – not
including Sundays and bad weather days – 81 580 716 oysters were fished; in 1906
the figure was 67 150 641; and in 1907 21 000 000 oysters were fished in 36 working
days. As a further instance of the wildly-fluctuating harvests of 1887, an oyster
bank five miles long by about one-and-a-half miles wide, with 600–700 oysters per
square yard, had a potential of around 164 000 000 oysters. A few months after the
survey not a single oyster remained – presumably all were destroyed by sea action.

At the age of four years the Sri Lankan oyster does not produce many
marketable pearls, but for those in their fifth and sixth years the numbers double,
and the output of seven-year-olds is said to quadruple. Eight years seems to be the
maximum oyster life span.

Pearl fishing notices

When a profitable oyster fishing was deemed possible, a notice would be published
in both English and Singhalese, giving details as shown on pp 39 and 40. A similar
notice would be given by the Indian authorities across the Gulf of Mannar. The
conditions in the temporary hutted villages and methods of fishing are similar.

FORT ST GEORGE (MADRAS, INDIA)

JANUARY 16, 1900

Notice is hereby given that a pearl fishery will take place at Veerapandianpatanam on or about the 12th March, 1900.

1. The bank to be fished is the Theradipulipudithapar, estimated to employ 100 boats for twenty days with average loads of 7,000 oysters per day.

2. It is therefore recommended that such boat owners and divers as may wish to be employed shall be at Tuticorin on or before 1st of March next and anchor their boats abreast of the government flagstaff; the first day's fishing will take place on the 12th of March, weather permitting.

3. The fishery will be conducted on account of Government, and the oysters put up for sale in such lots as may be deemed expedient.

4. The arrangements of the fishery will be the same as have been usual on similar occasions.

5. Payments to be made in ready money in rupees or in Government of India notes. *Checks on the Bank of Madras or Bank Agencies will be received on letters of credit being produced to warrant the drawing of such checks.

6. All particulars can be obtained on application to the Superintendent of Pearl Fisheries, Tuticorin.

Tinnevelly Collector's Office,   Sd/ J. P. BEDFORD

16th November 1899   Collector

* *Author's note:* The spelling of 'checks' is taken from the printed notice on page 131 of *The Book of the Pearl,* by Kunz and Stevenson. The variations of spelling of paars, pars, Mannar, Manaar occur with the Sri Lankan and Indian papers.

THE CEYLON COMPANY OF PEARL FISHERS LIMITED

NOTICE

It is hereby given that a Pearl Fishery will take place at Marichchukkaddi, in the island of Ceylon, on or about February 20th 1907.

The banks to be fished are:–

(1) The Karativu, Dutch Moderagam and Alanturai Pars, estimated to contain 21,000,000 oysters, sufficient to employ 100 boats for twenty-one days with average loads of 10,000 each per day.

The North-West and Mid-West Cheval, estimated to contain 2,000,000 oysters, sufficient to employ 100 boats for two days with average loads of 10,000 oysters.

The Muttuvaratu Par, estimated to contain 8,000,000 oysters, sufficient to employ 100 boats for eight days with average loads as before stated: each boat being fully manned with divers.

(2) It is notified that fishing will begin on the first favourable day after February 19 · Conditions governing the employment of divers will be given separately.

(3) Marichchukkaddi is on the mainland, eight miles by sea south of Sillavaturai, and good supplies of water and provisions can be obtained there.

(4) The Fishery will be conducted on account of the Ceylon Company of Pearl Fisheries Ltd and the oysters put up to sale in such lots as may be deemed expedient.

Australia

Pearl fishing started in Australia about 1861 and is thus comparatively new in comparison with that of the Red Sea, Persian Gulf and the Gulf of Mannar. The fisheries extend from Cooktown on the north east coast to Fremantle on the south west coast (*Figure 5.3*). Like many of the pearl discoveries there appeared at first to be inexhaustible supplies of shells, whether for mother-of-pearl or pearls, or both.

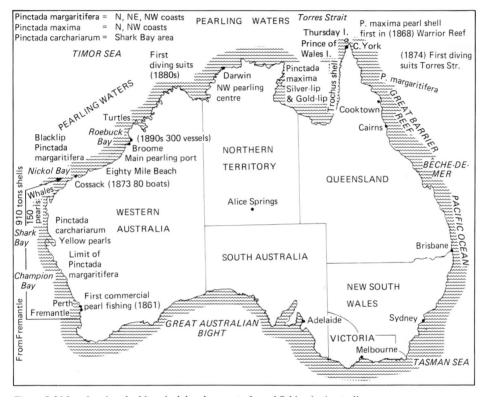

Figure 5.3 Map showing the historical development of pearl fishing in Australia

Three types of oyster are fished around the Australian coast, namely *Pinctada maxima*, *Pinctada margaritifera* and *Pinctada carchariarum*. The largest of the trio, *P. maxima*, grows in Australian waters up to 12 in in diameter with a weight of approximately 12 lb, and it was widest in distribution over the whole area. Originally it was sought for its mother-of-pearl content, pearls being a secondary bonus. Its shell is uniformly white and known as 'silver-lip' shell. It does not occur in densely populated beds but rather in a scattered manner on rocky reefs which extend for miles. Some 'gold-lip' shell is found in muddier conditions in narrow channels between islands of the north west coast.

P. margaritifera is a smaller oyster seldom measuring more than 8 in diameter, with a weight of around 2 lb; it is distinctive by reason of a black edge around the

interior perimeter of the shell and is termed 'black-lip'. It is not so plentiful as was
P. maxima but it is to be found thinly scattered around the Queensland and
Western Australia coasts to just below Shark Bay.

The various colours of 'silver', 'gold' and 'black' applied to the mantle are
probably due to protein in the food supply. Trace elements also can cause
colouring.

P. carchariarum, the smallest of Australia's pearl oysters, is similar in size to the
P. radiata of the Persian Gulf and is confined almost entirely to the Shark Bay area
of Western Australia. The shell lost its commercial importance for button-making
in competition with the Mississippi shell. The pearls found in this relatively small
oyster are of shades of yellow straw and occasionally a fine golden colour.

Changes due to supply, methods and labour

Considerable changes have taken place in Australian waters since the 1860 era;
over-fishing, no conservation, labour costs, all have played a part. Some details of
these attitudes and changes can be read in the sections below entitled 'Some aspects
of the Australian pearl trade' and 'The cultivation of pearls', pages 43 and 66
respectively.

In Western Australia, Broome is the pearl fishing centre; the headquarters of the
Northern Territory is Port Darwin. The Queensland pearling centre is Thursday
Island where Port Kennedy's prosperity depends mainly on pearl fishing despite its
obvious strategic position politically. Most of the labour force is non-white.

All pearl and shell fishing, and activities for pearl farming and cultivation, are
now undertaken with either full armoured diving dress or partial protection, i.e.
helmet and corselage only.

Considerable movement towards the fishing grounds in the Aru islands of the
Arafura Sea is now taking place. Indonesia together with New Guinea is fairly
productive of the large *P. maxima* shells.

In Australia various acts and laws were passed to govern the sizes of oysters
permitted to be fished, and there were certain prohibitions, but these laws were
difficult to enforce. In the early days of Australian pearl fishing when
mother-of-pearl was the profitable material, pearls tending to be regarded as a
bonus, it was difficult to prevent the theft of pearls since in Torres Strait vessels it
was considered that pearls were not part of the owner's income!

When fished, the shells were stored out of the sun to prevent the mother-of-pearl
from being affected. The surfaces of the shells were covered with marine growth and
coral encrustations which first had to be removed. The shells were opened by
placing the oyster hinge down on the deck and using a broad-bladed knife to sever
the adductor muscle. Pearls are sought by sight and touch in the soft part of the
oyster, the large being found in the mantle and the smaller seed pearls sometimes in
the adductor muscle tissue. Blisters on the pearl shell sometimes contain pearls;
even the blister itself is cut out for appropriate use. The soft parts of the oyster are
discarded and the shells are left to dry out, especially the ligament of the hinge.
This allows the shells to be parted without injury to the brittle mother-of-pearl.

The yellow pearls found in the *P. carchariarum* of Shark Bay reefs were fished by means of light dredges. After the shells have been opened with a knife, the soft parts are scooped out, placed in tubs, and allowed to putrefy under the hot sun. Sea-water is poured in and the whole mass stirred. After several days the now-disintegrated odorous mass is decanted to leave the pearls at the bottom of the tub. The smell generated by these activities is said to be similar to that of the 'washing toddies' of Marichchikadde in Mannar. Pearls of yellowish hues usually have a more ready sale in countries where the population's colouring and skin pigmentation are darker than in Europe generally.

Some aspects of the Australian pearl trade

An interesting account of Australian pearl and mother-of-pearl production is given under 'Pearl' in *The Australian Encyclopaedia*.

Something over a hundred years ago the early days of pearl fishing were devoted principally to the gathering of mother-of-pearl shell, and any pearls accidentally discovered were treated as a bonus. *P. maxima,* the largest of marine oysters, supplied both gold-lip and silver-lip pearl shell to 80 per cent of the world market, chiefly in America. In 1955, 1300 tons of shell were sold for £770 000. Originally, mother-of-pearl shells had been used by aborigines for ornamentation and ceremonial purposes and no value was attached to pearls as such.

Commercial pearl fishing began in 1861 when J. and W. Bateman of Fremantle sent their boat the *Flying Foam,* skippered by one James Turner, to the vicinity of Nickol Bay, Western Australia, near the settlement of Cossack. They gathered 910 tons of shell and 150 pearls. In 1867 an American sailor named Taye found aborigines gathering shells by hand at low tide and he introduced them to skin-diving from dinghies. Both male and female aborigines participated in diving to depths up to ten fathoms (60 ft), but later, when regulations forbade women divers, other divers came from Timor and Java. By 1873 more than 80 boats were pearling out of Cossack.

Diving suits were first used in north western Australia in the 1880s, and in Torres Strait the first pearl shell was fished in 1868 from Warrior Reef, where diving dress proper was first used by white divers in 1874.

In 1877 109 pearling vessels (63 with apparatus) working from island bases and Somerset settlement on Cape York, were officially operated from Port Kennedy on Thursday Island, the main port for Torres Strait and North Queensland pearling.

Towards the end of the last century there was an influx of Japanese divers who worked diligently for the Australian companies, and since few white men seemed suited for such work, preferring shore-based jobs, the Japanese became the principal operatives.

During the 1890s Broome, another Western Australian port, with some 300 vessels on Roebuck Bay, superseded Cossack as the main pearling port. The price of pearl shell in 1903 was £95 a ton, and from London, Paris and New York, pearl buyers descended upon Broome, where the population by 1910 was 4000 people. A Singhalese, T. B. Ellis, gained fame when he rose from the ranks as a pearl cleaner to become reputedly the world's best 'pearl doctor'.

After the Second World War, which in 1941 had enforced the withdrawal of Japanese labour and prohibition of the export of mother-of-pearl shell, the industry was in a poor state. Reorganization took place but met with many difficulties. Among the participants were Torres Strait islanders, Malays and Australian aborigines. In 1952 a shortage of experts caused the Australian pearlers to bring back a limited number of Japanese. By 1955 the industry employed 168 of them together with 906 Torres Strait islanders, 152 aborigines, 16 half-castes, 61 Europeans, 24 Okinawans, 63 Chinese, 95 Malays, 85 Indonesians and one Filipino.

Ninety diving vessels off the Torres Strait and east coast of Queensland were gathering *Trochus niloticus* shell and pearl shell. The West Australian coast had 35 boats and Northern Territory waters had ten boats operating from Darwin. The north western Australian pearling grounds extend from Exmouth Gulf to Cape Londonderry. Reefs, rip tides and whirlpools in the area make diving dangerous, but divers on the north west coast now wear full heavy suit, boots, helmet, etc, though Torres Strait divers use only the helmet and corselet.

Most shell is obtained at less than 20 fathoms (120 ft) but some of it is fished from 40 fathoms, at which depth the water pressure is 53 lb/in^2 (as against the surface air pressure of less than 15 lb/in^2). Work at such a pressure is limited to half-an-hour to one hour. Between 1909 and 1917 there were 145 known deaths from divers' paralysis (bends). Shark attacks are rare but in 1899 50 pearling vessels were destroyed in a cyclone with the loss of 300 men drowned.

In 1949 a standard type of pearling vessel was proposed by the Commonwealth Fisheries Office. It was to be 58 ft overall with a beam of 14'9" and draught of 6'6" with a cruiser stern, and for easier handling the staysail was to be dispensed with in favour of a Bermuda rig.

Peak pearl production figures at £100 000 in 1912 dropped to a low of £10 000 in 1951. Later figures are not given but the present-day high prices paid for natural pearls make £100 000 look quite a modest sum of money.

The South Seas

Among the many palm-tree-bedecked coral islands of the South Pacific, the various groups known collectively as the South Sea Islands are: the Society Islands, the Marquesas, New Caledonia and the Tuamotu Islands.

Tahiti is the largest of the Society Islands and is the focal point of the pearl trade, although few pearls are produced from Tahiti itself. The main source of pearls is the archipelago of Tuamotu, Gambier and Tubai, which are sometimes termed the Pearl Islands. Tahiti is luxuriously verdant with food in abundance whereas the coral-reef formation of the Tuamotu Islands produces very little vegetation. The oysters are the black-lip *P. margaritifera* which grow to a larger-than-average size.

The oyster beds are very extensive, occurring in protected lagoons with coral beds at varying depths affording ideal conditions for development. The richest reefs are at Hikueru (Melville Island), and it is said that almost half of the total output of the archipelago comes from this source.

William Reed, in his book *Huîtres Perliéres de Polynesie,* gives (on page 27) facts and figures of mother-of-pearl production from 1951 to 1971 (*Figure 5.4*).

Before the First World War, artisans in Paris produced most of the engraved souvenirs from Tahitian mother-of-pearl. Shells were also used for occupational work in camps for foreign and/or political internees. The Tahitians, who used mother-of-pearl for lures and fish hooks, did not enter the souvenir or curio market until 1946.

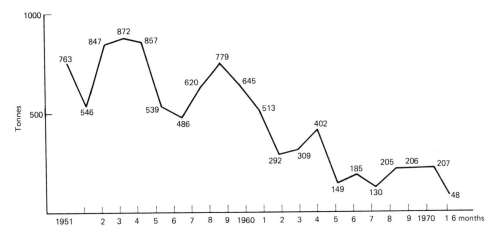

Figure 5.4 Mother-of-pearl export figures from Polynesia 1951–1971 (after W. Reed)

When the territorial or islands control passed to the French government in 1880, even then the extensive fishing for mother-of-pearl and pearls had depleted the oyster beds, such that the French Ministry of Marine and Colonies instituted an investigation into the condition of and possible improvement to the industry.

The cultivation of oysters was suggested by Dr Bouchon-Brandley in 1870 because each diver was taking 200 kg of oysters each day. A method of collecting spat of *P. margaritifera* (black-lip) on faggots of wood or branches of trees was practised by M. Simon Grand (an oyster breeder from Arcachon). These experiments took place in Gambier but lapsed due to lack of government fundings and little further interest was shown in oyster culture.

In 1953 a Professor G. Ranson of the Natural History Museum, Paris, spent seven months in the territory, particularly at Hikueru where he personally collected spat at various depths. Although he could not prolong his stay and investigate the results of his work, he recommended the employment of a specialist and proposed the creation of reserves in each lagoon for breeding purposes, and/or the division of lagoons into sectors which would be fished under a four-year rotation plan.

The Fisheries Service undertook in 1954 the regulation of mother-of-pearl fishing and instituted a semi-nursery where young oysters taken from a prolific source were sown in zones where they could grow under ideal conditions. This method currently followed in the Tuamotu Islands is showing an improvement in shell production.

The Philippines and Malaysian Archipelago areas

The Philippine Islands (*Figure 5.5*) which embrace the Sulu Sea and Sulu
Archipelago have been renowned for fine pearls for hundreds of years. The Sulu
shell is very beautiful and has a yellowish border to the rim. *P. maxima* is the chief
producer of shell and fine pearls as well as *P. margaritifera* (black-lip) in lesser
quantities.

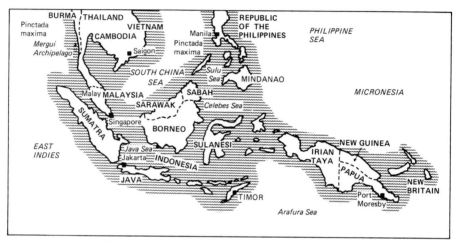

Figure 5.5 Map of the Phillipines and Malaysian Archipelago areas

Thanks to the strong protective attitude of Hadji Mohamam Jamoul Kiriam, the
Sultan of Sulu, the United States government preserved the fishing rights of Moro
province shortly after the Spanish-American war of 1904–1906. Two kinds of
licence became necessary: (1) for fishing with armoured diving dress, as early as
1905, and (2) for nude fishing, i.e. no armoured diving suits. The Sulu pearl divers
(nude), who enter the water feet first before turning to dive and swim to the
bottom, are said to be among the best in the world.

The pearly nautilus (*Nautilus pompilius*) also occasionally contributes yellow-
coloured pearls. This cephalopod mollusc has a beautiful nacreous lining to its
several chambers and apart from the pearls it may or may not produce, its shell is
sometimes stripped of its outer porcellaneous layers to reveal its true beauty and is
used as an *object d'art* when mounted in precious metal (A. E. Farn, *Journal of
Gemmology*). Originally, piratical activity precluded accurate knowledge of pearl
and shell production in these areas.

P. maxima is still fished in fairly abundant quantities, particularly from the
Mindanao Sea which is used as a supply source for shells for pearl culture. It seems
that all South Seas and Malaysian waters, including those from Indonesia to New
Guinea (Papua), which are prolific in oyster shell such as *P. maxima* and *P.
margaritifera,* are not only sources of very fine *natural pearls* but also, by virtue of
their ability to sustain large oyster growth, lend themselves to the intrusion of
man-made *cultured-pearl* farms.

The pearls of the Americas (*Figure 5.6*)

Panama

When the Spanish explorer Balboa crossed the Isthmus of Panama in 1513 he discovered the Gulf of St Michael, now the Gulf of Panama. He was presented by a local Indian chief with over 200 large pearls, some of which were yellow, some blue, some black, and others a metallic green. The Indians told of an island named Tararequi (the Island of Pearls) where even larger pearls could be found. This island is about 8° above the equator in the Gulf of Panama, and there the Indians fished for the Spaniards, although it was not the season, and found fine white pearls. The Spaniards sent 550 men to subdue the island and forced a levy of 100 marcs (800 ounces) of pearls to be paid annually to the King of Spain.

Some very large fine pearls weighing over 100 grains were found, many of which made their way to the Spanish courts and cathedrals. A report published in Venezia in 1719 (*Giro del Mondo*) by the Italian traveller Gemelli-Careri, who visited Panama in 1697, said that the local pearls were equal to the pearls of the then Ceylon, and later, in 1735, a Spanish admiral stated that there were still plenty available and that the local slave owners kept a few of their slaves permanently employed at pearl fishing. At that time most of the pearls were going to Lima (Peru) where they were greatly appreciated.

The pearl reefs of Panama extend along the Pacific coast from east of the Bay of Panama almost as far as Costa Rica, and although this is a vast area, not all of the reefs yield pearls. The main source is the Pearl Islands, a group of sixteen islands near to the Pacific terminal of the Panama Canal. Mother-of-pearl shell is an important part of the pearling life which fluctuates according to market conditions. Huge quantities were exported to England between 1855 and 1859.

Expeditions from other countries tried their fortunes in the area, importing a diving bell and air pumps, but sickness, storms and yellow fever soon ended these attempts. Sometimes the early apparatus was faulty. The oyster in the Panamanian fisheries, *Pinctada mazatlanica,* is larger than the Venezuelan and has a shell of much better quality from a commercial point of view.

Pearls are a secondary product after shell but they are nevertheless keenly sought. Nowadays, most of the pearls go to Paris, chiefly because of existing trade relations with established credits. However, through the trade commercial channels the pearls eventually appear in other world capitals.

Venezuela

Pearls from this area tested at the London Chamber of Commerce Laboratory by the endoscope method were notable because of their glassy appearance which was much enhanced when their interiors were illuminated by the powerful beam of light from the inclined 45° mirror of the endoscope needle.

Pinctada radiata, the Venezuelan oyster, is slightly smaller than the *Pinctada martensi* of Japan, and about half the size of *P. mazatlanica* of Mexico.

Columbus in his voyages was the first European to discover pearls in the waters of the Americas, and he found them on the islands of Margarita and Cubagua, just

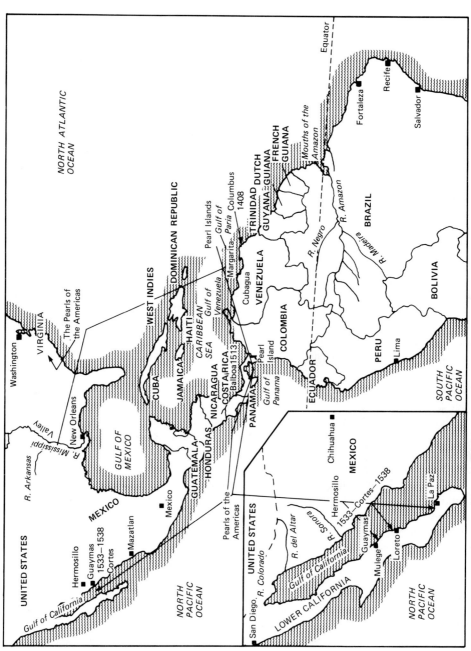

Figure 5.6 Pearling areas of Central and South America and those of Virginia and Mississippi in North America

off the northern coast of Venezuela, when sailing westwards from the Gulf of Paria. However, it appears that for some reason he failed to report his discovery and when sailors returned to Spain with many fine pearls, there was some anger at court which resulted in his return in chains. Eventually he was believed and reconciled with Queen Isabella. Meanwhile, King Ferdinand had sent another sea captain, Pedro Alonso Lino, to exploit Columbus' finds in Cubagua. This he did, returning with over 90 lb of round, lustrous and quite sizeable pearls. The village on the island was named New Cadiz and became the first pearling colony to be set up in that area by Europeans.

Unfortunately, the Spaniards forced the enslaved natives to dive from dawn to dusk on poor food and under bad conditions. Consequently, pearls accumulated when divers could no longer be found, but by the time Columbus died in 1506 laws had been passed to restrict the amount of work and to feed and cloth the divers.

Further westwards on the Venezuelan coast pearls were found to such an extent that America was regarded as a place where pearls came from. The Cubaguan pearls were small in size and fairly prolific, but excessive fishing, together with the use of rakes and dredges, began to take its toll. In 1851 pearls were still being shipped to Spain in fair numbers; a note in 1597 states that 350 lb of pearls were shipped.

Early in the 17th century imitation pearls were undermining the value of pearls, as was the attraction of Peruvian and Mexican mining ventures. By 1823, following the overthrow of the Spanish government, other peoples were bidding for fishing rights. Venezuela became independent in 1829 and taxes rose and pearling was abandoned in 1833.

A dormant period favoured the replenishment of the sources of supply. A few years following saw good marketing but the use of dredges again depleted the fisheries, which remained poorly due to heavy taxes and constant changes in regulations.

At the turn of the century the Venezuelan authorities arranged a programme of defined areas of fishing concessions tied to a set percentage on the proceeds. Venezuela continues to this day to produce a supply of pearls, which range in colour from white to grey and in metallic hues of bronze and black.

The method of diving remained basically similar to that employed elsewhere, namely, nude diving with attached stone weight to assist descent, a knife, and a sack around the waist for the catch. There is a prejudice against diving suits (armour). Many pearl fishers use dredges which they claim allow the smaller oysters to be avoided and/or spread the area of the oyster beds.

In 1983 the present author was privileged to examine radiographs of undrilled pearls of small sizes, said to come from Venezuela. The colours were mostly light metallic bronze and grey.

Mexico

Following the conquest of Mexico by Hernando Cortes in 1521, the existence of pearls on the western shores of Mexico was revealed. Cortes explored the Pacific coast of Mexico (1533–1538) and found evidence of prolific pearl resources. Huge quantities were secured in what is now Hermosillo in the State of Sonora.

Spanish expeditions specially fitted out for pearl-seeking treated the Indians badly and aroused much bitter feeling towards the Spaniards. In 1642 Jesuit missionaries obtained better conditions and working relations for the Indians to an extent that later colonists were able to fish without fear. Yaqui and Mayo Indians were the skilful divers.

The improved conditions soon found the soldiers and sailors of the Spanish forces engaged more with pearling than with their official duties. In 1704 a law was passed prohibiting soldiers or sailors from pearl fishing activities; later laws and restrictions concentrated much business into comparatively few hands. At Mulege, on the eastern coast of Lower California, a single dealer in 1743 marketed 127 lb of pearls and in 1744 he marketed 275 lb.

Although one-fifth of all pearls were considered the royal revenue, reports of the amounts and/or value vary in their importance. Doubtless the fifth suffered deprivations en route to the Royal Court. One report by a Jesuit priest, following the expulsion of his order from Mexico in 1767, gave a very low figure of revenue and doubted if many people employed in the pearl industry really made much money. Certainly there was a sharp decline from the heyday of 1744.

When Mexico became independent in 1821, promoters with various schemes sought to enter the pearling industry, using more up-to-date methods. One such London-based promotion under a Lieutenant Harvey, exploring the Gulf of California in 1825, stated that few shells were found and that natives seemed unreliable. Harvey noted the scarcity of shells, particularly on the coast of Sonora, and that north of 28°30′ none were found. This accords somewhat with an observation by D. S. M. Field in an article 'Pearls of the seas and oceans', in *The Canadian Gemmologist* (1982) in which he says: 'The gem pearl beds of the seas and of the oceans lie, as a rule, within 25°N and 25°S latitudes'. Field quotes, further, the Japanese *Pinctada martensi* as a notable exception.

The small village of Loreto on the California coast of the Gulf was at that time the pearl centre with La Paz in secondary role. The expedition of 1825 found the diving bells useless in rough weather, whilst in calm weather the uneven sea-bed and strong undercurrents made it difficult to operate the diving bell. The enterprise was abandoned after three years.

From 1830 mother-of-pearl shell became a commercial viability, the price rising from 600 francs per tonne in Paris to 2000 francs per tonne in 1854. In 1857 the Mexican government divided the Gulf area into four parts, only one part to be fished per year, and the concession was to be rented out to the highest bidder for the season from May to the end of September.

Following lack of success with the diving bell, all pearl fishing up to 1874 had been done by nude divers, but in 1874 two boats from England and Australia equipped with modern armoured diving suts, air pumps, etc, were very successful, operating in deeper water than the nude divers could attempt. At first many accidents happened but gradually nude divers were put out of business by the use of diving suits.

In 1884 exclusive concessions to various parts of the ocean floor on the Mexican and Californian coasts were granted which, together with earlier ancient rights, soon found little space left for further development. No accurate figures of pearl production from these concessions are available.

More systematic methods of working now obtain in deeper waters from large boats and shore-based camps. Although nude diving in the warm periods from mid May to October still occurs as a form of cheap labour, the main source of supply is from the commercially-financed diving apparatus.

The oyster fished in the Gulf of California, on the Pacific coast of Mexico and the eastern coast of Lower California, is *P. mazatlanica* which is similar to the black-lip oyster of Australian waters. It is found particularly in the reefs which range for 300 miles between Mulege, about halfway down the Gulf, and Cap San Lucas at the southern end of Lower California. *Margaritifera (Avicula) vinesi* used to be prolific in the Gulf close to the mouth of the Colorado River and probably this area was the source of the 1743 yield of superb pearls. Many very fine pearls have been fished in the Gulf of California, and one of the finest was found at Mulege in 1884. It weighed 372 grains. A 400-grain pearl found near Loreto became the property of the Queen of Spain.

Virginia and the Mississippi valley

In the churchyard of Bow Church, Cheapside, London (Sir Christopher Wren, 1680) stands an emotive statue of a sea captain/privateer. He resembles Sir Francis Drake, but is in fact Captain John Smith who is described on the plinth as 'Citizen and Cordwainer 1580–1631. First among the leaders of the settlement at Jamestown, Virginia, from which began the expansion of the English-speaking peoples.'

Captain John Smith was a tough adventurer. Born at Willoughby, Lincolnshire, he sought action and found time to fight in Hungary against the Turks; he fought for the Duke of Austria. Later he became a merchant/pirate, was captured and sold as a slave but escaped and fought against Spanish men-of-war. Finally he joined a company expedition from London to colonize Virginia in 1605 (Jamestown was founded in 1607 on the James River).

Smith was captured by Powhattan, the powerful Indian chief who controlled a confederacy of 30 tribes, and his life was spared only by the intervention of Pocahontas, the chief's daughter. A contemporary picture of her can be seen on page 66 of Joan Younger Dickinson's *The Book of Pearls*. Pocahontas married John Rolfe of Jamestown in 1614, returned with him to England, and is buried in the graveyard at St George's Church, Gravesend, Kent. Descendants of her son Thomas still live in Virginia.

Captain John Smith wrote of the importance attached to pearls by some of the tribes, particularly as tributes.

The pearls of the Virginian Indians were probably from mussels and oysters and the aboriginal use of the pearls was considerable, pearl ear pendants being worn by both sexes and they were buried with their owners at death. Powhattan, in his 60-yards-long treasure house at Orapaks, had it piled high with pearls and copper.

Although there is no record of pearls from North America having reached Europe in the 16th and 17th centuries, there were undoubtedly large numbers owned by the various tribes and interred in the burial mounds of the Indians.

Though many pearls traded among the Indians came from the Gulf of Mexico, large quantities certainly came from inland lakes and rivers. The rivers of the Mississippi valley have been prolific sources of pearls, some of which have been extremely fine.

It is unfortunate that the lustre of numerous large pearls was damaged by heat. The usual manner of opening clams/mussels was to heat them in fire cinders, boiling water, etc. The Indians would heat the shellfish until considered fit to eat and any pearl would drop out, or would have already fallen out, with consequent dire results to its lustre. The first remarkable find was in a supper of fried mussels of a pearl around 400-grain size; it was spoiled by heat.

The pearls of North America first appreciated in price around the middle of the 19th century; these were freshwater pearls originating from near Paterson, New Jersey. A local carpenter, searching the same area, found a Pink Pearl weighing 93 grains; it was bought by Tiffany of New York for $1500. It travelled profitably to Paris to become the property of Empress Eugénie and was known as the 'Queen Pearl'. Following this valuable discovery, gold-rush conditions took over in the area around Notch Brook and after a few years every mussel had been removed. However, the quest for pearls continued and a few were found in the Little Miami River at Waynesville, Ohio.

The pearling industry began to move westwards and southwards to Kentucky and Tennessee and finally to the stupendous finds in the Upper Mississippi valley (*Figure 5.6*). South west Winsconsin in the late 19th century produced pink, purple and metallic green pearls; 93 pearls fetched £11 700 in London in 1890. In Tennessee the rivers Clinch, Cumberland and Tennessee provided good supplies of pearls while in Arkansas the White, St Francis and Arkansas Rivers, and practically every stream, yielded pearls, fishing being made easy by the low-water conditions at that time. The White and Black Rivers, with the pearling industry focused at Black Rock, supported a thousand people in an area stretching over twenty miles. At its height it is said that 10 000 people were engaged in the pearling industry in Arkansas.

The River Mississippi was a deeper-water prospect. Pearls were not found so plentifully as in other areas but the huge supplies of shell made button manufacturing from the lack-lustre shell a profitable industry. Shell-gathering for the mother-of-pearl industry from the Mississippi, Arkansas, White, Wabash, Ohio, Illinois and St Francis Rivers, added to the actual pearl yield. The value of the mother-of-pearl from the Mississippi River valley was at that time $20 per ton, compared with $1200 per ton for Australian pearl shell. The pearl-bearing lakes, ponds and rivers of North America from Maine, Massachusetts, New York State, Pennsylvania, Maryland, Georgia, Virginia, etc, plus all of the associated states of the Mississippi River, have been fished by amateurs under gold-rush conditions and by professionals using water telescopes, drags and rakes of varying designs.

Most of the shell of the Mississippi mussels are for mother-of-pearl use, i.e. button-making. At one time 35 000 tons of shell were produced annually from the Mississippi, i.e., twice the amount of shell from all other parts of the world. The mother-of-pearl shell was found by the Japanese to be ideal for the manufacture of spherical beads for use as nuclei in the production of whole cultured pearls. It was used because biologically it was 'acceptable' to the treated oyster, being chemically similar to the shell lining of the cultured oyster. More important though, from a production point of view, it was of a cold, grey, lack-lustre quality which did not exert any colour influence through the relatively thin skin of the cultured pearl. Wars, embargoes and restraints have made the use of Mississippi mother-of-pearl nuclei more difficult. Other shell is now used when possible.

The sizes, shapes and colours of pearls fished from the freshwater sources of North America, particularly those of the Mississippi River valley area, range from a matt white colour to faint shades of pink, yellow and salmon, and then grades of purple, copper and red and other metallic colours, steely blue and bronze being not unusual. Dog-tooth pearl shapes (*Figure 5.7*) are typical of the Mississippi, as are wing pearls. Baroque shapes are the commonest but fine round pearls have often been found. A necklace of 38 pearls weighing 1710 grains was formed in 1904 with an average weight of 45 grains per pearl. It fetched 500 000 francs when sold in Paris.

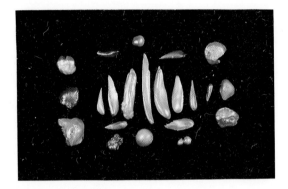

Figure 5.7 Dog-tooth and wing pearls from Mississippi (Photo: B W Anderson)

The early finds of large pearls in fairly large shells in many of the states of North America were probably due to the fact that in general the local population did not seek shellfish for food and if they did, they preferred the smaller, younger shellfish to the large shellfish which would be coarser eating. Thus, many pearls were allowed long, uninterrupted growth. When the gold-rush conditions occurred every mussel and oyster was swept from its habitat and in a few years the prolific sources became denuded. It seems certain that unless steps are taken towards conservation and fishing of regulated areas with accompanying close seasons, even the prodigious sources of North America will be killed off.

Freshwater pearls

Freshwater pearls are found in pearl mussels in rivers, lakes and ponds, the name *Margaritifera* now being generally used to describe them. They are slow in growth, taking six years to reach maturity, and live for periods varying from fifteen to fifty years.

The invasion of Britain by Julius Caesar in 54 BC is said to have been due partly to an appreciation of the pearls found there. Today the chief source, and a very small one, is Scotland. As is often the case, on reading details of sources of pearls, many areas are described and often the termination of such a description is '. . . but they are now fished out'. Although the production of pearls from Scottish rivers, lakes and ponds is small and comparatively unimportant, as recently as August 1967 a fine-quality, good-shaped pearl was fished from Scotland's River Tay by the professional pearl fisher Bill Abernethy.

The Abernethy pearl

Bill's pearl is now known as the 'Abernethy pearl' (*Colour plate 24*) and can be seen at the establishment of A. & G. Cairncross in Perth, Scotland. It is 11.5 mm in diameter and weighs 43.6 grains. Its colour has a hint of lilac with a beautiful lustre. Another pearl found later is 9.3 mm in diameter, weighs 22.8 grains, and has been named 'Wilhelmina' in deference to the Abernethy pearl which is known as 'Little Willie'.

Instances of spectacular pearl finds can cause an excitement and renewed interest, but generally freshwater pearls do not command the same esteem and financial appreciation as their sea-water counterparts from oysters.

It is true that in a quieter, subdued quality they have considerable appeal, and though comparisons are odious, it must be said that the higher prices obtained by the much more prolific oyster pearls are a weighty factor in 'appreciation'.

Oriental and freshwater pearls

The term 'pearl' on its own covers both freshwater and sea-water natural pearls. Similarly, the term 'jade' covers the two materials nephrite and jadeite, but the trade places the higher price and appreciation on that which is truly oriental. There are still sources of mussels which have a nacreous lining and could yield pearls under suitable conditions. Some sources are used for their mother-of-pearl, and others for cultured-pearl production.

Probably the most prolific source of freshwater mussels is the Mississippi valley with its various rivers flowing into or adjacent to the River Mississippi. These are described as the North American section of the sources of pearls. Another fertile area is Lake Biwa in Shiga Province, Honshu, Japan, where the mussel is *Hyriopsis schlegeli,* a large variety used entirely for the production of cultured pearls by means of a tissue graft (insertion) method which has a prolific yield.

Fluorescence of freshwater pearls

Whether they be freshwater natural pearls or the product of cultivation with nuclei or not, all these freshwater-origin pearls and cultured pearls have trace elements in their chemical composition. That element is manganese which has the effect of causing marked fluorescence and phosphorescence in these products under the stimulation of X-ray excitation. This is still a useful characteristic in diagnosing cultured or natural pearls.

Conservation of mussel beds

Quite a few rivers in Scotland yield mussel pearls. The careful rotation of fishing various grounds by knowledgeable people such as Bill Abernethy allows for future crops.

The rivers of Europe also have been well-known with established markets for their produce but like many other sources they are no longer so prolific or worthwhile. Correspondence from Germany voiced doubts upon the viability of freshwater pearl potential, quoting pollution and haphazard activities as causes of diminution. The gathering of mussels of all sizes soon depletes the beds. If one could generalize, it would be to suggest to would-be pearl fishers that they gather only large, rough and distorted shells and to leave the small and medium sizes to increase. Tread warily and avoid damage to young growth.

French pearls

In France the River Vologne in Lorraine has long been known as an historical source of freshwater pearls. In 1862 the Empress Eugénie had mussels from the Vologne transported to the ponds at Malmaison with a hope for pearl production, but no records exist of any success.

In the West of France small pearls of good colour were found in the rivers, particularly at their confluences. Many rivers are constantly being quoted and re-quoted by authors from the great work by Kunz and Stevenson onwards. In France at Billiers in Brittany both Dubois and Jameson in 1901 and 1902 respectively confirmed pearl formation in the edible mussel as being due to the intrusion of parasitic larval worms.

Russian pearls

In most European countries where mussel pearls were found in streams and rivers, considerable dwindling of supplies of pearls has been noted. The Russians especially had a great liking for pearls. Many pearls from river mussels seldom left the areas in which they were found. Even today it is possible that in such a vast territory as Russia there may be undisturbed streams and lakes where hoards of mussels bearing pearls slowly grow and die, or even eject their burdensome intrusion to the river or lake bed.

Freshwater mussels have proved to be singularly tough in accepting man-made nuclei, whether they can be the flat, lead Buddhas of the Chinese of the diced tissue cubes of the Lake Biwa operators. It would not be surprising to find a process of non-nucleated cultured pearl production taking place in Russian waters. Certainly from an external appearance there is great difficulty for the dealer in freshwater natural pearls to distinguish them from the non-nucleated cultured pearls from freshwater mussels.

Chinese pearls

In China today there is a considerable production of non-nucleated cultured pearls from freshwater mussels. They are said by one authority to be wrinkled and of poor quality but that the production is enormous. Like many other facets of China, little is reflected in general knowledge or trade hand-outs. Certainly historically the Chinese have had a love and appreciation of pearls and enjoyed a skilful manipulation of pearl-bearing mussels. Their production of pearl-coated objects in the 13th century reveals this knowledge and aptitude. One of the earliest of books, the Shu King (2350–625 BC) notes that pearls found in oysters from the River Hwai were given as tribute to Emperor Yu.

Cristaria plicatus was replaced in 1924 in Lake Biwa experiments in pearl cultivation by *Hyriopsis schlegeli*. It is possible that the Chinese use both types for their cultivation, and obviously they must equally be a source of natural freshwater pearls. The increase in demand for natural pearls, and thus the increase of X-ray photography experienced in the laboratory, saw the study of pearl structures much more keenly noted in the last few years than ever before. Many new sources were being investigated, particularly in Indonesia and probably China.

Other pearl-producing molluscs

In addition to pearl-bearing oysters and mussels, there are other molluscs which produce pearls. Among these are the huge *Strombus gigas* from which Pink Pearls originate, the giant clam *Tridacna gigas,* producer of the counterpart 'white' pearls, and the *Haliotis* and its abalone pearl.

The yellowish pearl found in the pearly nautilus has already been mentioned on page 46. The pearly nautilus is a cephalopod which, having a head, is fairly high in the order of molluscs *Tetrabranchiata*.

Strombus gigas is a huge univalve gastropod (so called because it moves on its stomach by means of a flat, muscular foot) which can measure up to 12 in in length and weigh from 5 to 6 lb. It appears in Bahamian and West Indian waters, on the Florida coasts and in the Gulf of California. Although the Pink Pearl found in *Strombus gigas* (*Colour plate 2*) has a *non*-nacreous exterior it nevertheless has a distinctive 'flame pattern' resembling watered silk. The colour of the pearl reflects the interior colour of the shell. Few of these pearls are found; fewer still are commercially important; yet a fine, good-sized and well-shaped specimen will command an appropriately good price.

The term 'Pink Pearl' with the capital initial letters is the correct written style for these products, as defined by CIBJO rules. This is to distinguish these non-nacreous conch pearls from pink-hued pearls of nacreous origin. Pink Pearls can be mistaken for pale pink coral, but their surface structure and superior density establish the difference.

The pink-hued shell has many uses, e.g. it makes an acceptable curio ornament, and it is carved for cameo-making, where the two colours of pink and white serve to accentuate each other. At one time it was used as a base for the manufacture of porcelain, and thousands of tons of it used to pass through Liverpool docks annually.

Tridacna gigas, described as 'The Giant Clam', is said to be the largest and heaviest shell in existence. It is a bivalve found in the Pacific and Indian Oceans and near reefs off the northern coast of Australia. No regular fishery occurs for this mollusc which can reach the prodigious weight of 500 lb.

The author, having often read of clam-seeking fisherman wading in tropical waters getting their legs trapped in the 'jaws' of these monster shells, was startled to find that this was a real possibility. Early in 1984 BBC2 television screened a series titled 'Travellers in Time' which comprised archive films from the Royal Geographical Society. Included was a black-and-white film, 'Pearls and Savages', taken on a 1921 expedition to New Guinea (Papua) which showed pearls from opened oysters (*Pinctada maxima?*) and, more remarkably, a strong sapling was seen being snapped by the closing valves of the giant clam *Tridacna gigas.* By comparing boat sizes, people and diameter of the sapling, one could imagine the impossibility of a man extricating himself from such a perilous position, short of severing a trapped limb. Pearls from this monstrous clam are dull, non-nacreous and often quite large.

A description of *Tridacna gigas* by B. W. Anderson appears on pages 206–208 of the *Journal of Gemmology* (1971), and on pages 219–225 of the same issue of the journal E. H. Rutland gives in 'The constituents of pearls' a useful informative article with photomicrographs depicting pearl structure.

Reverting to *Tridacna gigas,* in contrast to its horrific ability to trap the unwary, its large beautiful shell is used sometimes as a benitier – a holy-water font. A pair of benitiers are said to have been the gift of the Republic of Venice to Francis I for use in the Church of St. Sulpice in Paris. In a French textbook a chapter on pearls has a sub-title 'Bivalves', under which heading is itemized 'Benitier'.

The *Haliotidae* are univalve molluscs and those from the cold waters of the Channel Islands coasts are termed 'ormer' or 'ear shells' and have slight ornamental value as such; scientifically, they are termed *Haliotis tuberculata.* The New Zealand variety is more beautiful and used extensively in jewellery/ornamentation. Its highly iridescent mother-of-pearl is termed 'Paua' shell; few baroque pearls are produced. In the Gulf of California are found some of the finest *Haliotids* the pearls from which are known as 'abalone' pearls, and they are vividly coloured in greens, yellows and blues. They are found also on the Florida coast of the USA, the Queensland coast of Australia and in Japanese and Korean waters. The Japanese term them 'awabi'.

The abalone pearls are mostly of a hollow nature, lacking the concentric nacreous layers of oriental pearls; they are said to have an 'alveolar structure'. They have a low density but their striking appearance seldom requires a density test to be carried out to identify them. A radiograph of an abalone (*Haliotis*) pearl, part of an ear pendant, is seen in *Figure 5.8.* The hollow nature can be seen, together with the metal (gold) cap and metal peg securing the pearl. Haliotis shells, apart from their beautiful mother-of-pearl quality, are identified by a series of holes which allow water to flow through to the respiratory organs. As the shell grows in size the holes at one extremity tend to close, which gives the appearance of holes of ascending sizes. Attempts were made to cultivate pearls in the haliotis, according to Louis Bouton writing in *Comptes Rendus de l'Académie des Sciences* (1898). La Place Bostwick describes in *The Gemmologist* (1936) his experiments in growing pearls from abalones. At the Scripps Institution of Oceanography (at La Jolla, California) pearls are said to have been produced by insertion of a nacre nucleus into the body of the abalone (as it is termed on the California coast). The author is said to have produced cultured pearls from both freshwater and salt-water shell sources.

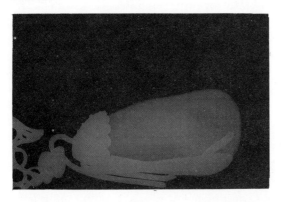

Figure 5.8 Radiograph of an abalone pearl ear pendant (Photo: A E Farn)

Pinna seminuda is the name of a bivalve mollusc which occasionally produces reddish or orange-hued pearls from Mediterranean sources; they are also reported from New Caledonia as being dark red to black in colour. They are said to be more highly crystalline than most pearls and by Jean P. Poirot, the Director of the Paris Laboratory, to have a fibrous radiating structure analagous to that of spherical boules of marcasite. Pinna pearls are found in *Pinna seminuda* according to Kunz and Stevenson and *Pinna nobilis* by J. P. Poirot. The description of the shape of the shell varies from fan-shaped to jambonneau (knuckle of ham) – both have similarities in broad outline. These red/brown pearls have only local value but have been fished since ancient times. The shells are variously described as 'sea-wings', 'wing shells' and 'silkworms of the sea'; the last undoubtedly springs from the use made of the silky fibres (byssus) with which the pinna secures an anchorage. The long silky fibres were washed, corded and made into gloves etc, with a finish similar to the iridescent colours seen on the backs of some beetles. The shells are found with their narrow ends partially embedded in sand and are lifted by means of a two-pronged fork device, or sometimes are hauled up by a type of noose.

Placenta placenta is known as the 'window-pane' oyster, and it has been termed the *'vitre chinoise'* by some. It has been fished in Tablegram Bay, north-east Sri Lanka, Pados Bay, Borneo and Kakinada Bay on the Madras coast of India. According to Professor James Hornell its pearls are originated by the same parasitic intrusion as that which produces the Gulf of Mannar pearl. The pearls are of a dull leaden colour (according to Kunz and Stevenson). Other authorities, dealing with the Indian sources, state that the pearls are used in India as medicine and that the shell is burned and used as lime. The same report describes the yield of pearls in various sizes of oyster from 50 mm to 160 mm. These yield pearls of which

47 per cent are smaller than 1 mm and 45 per cent are between 1 mm and 2 mm. The remaining 8 per cent are over 2 mm but few reach any size worth recording except for 3 mm, 4 mm and 7 mm sized pearls which were irregular or spindle-shaped. They are also decribed as 'bright and lustrous' which contrasts sharply with the 'dull leaden hue' of Kunz and Stevenson. In the Gulf of Arima they are found by the Japanese who term them 'taira gai'.

The appellation *'vitre chinoise'* is due to the transparency of the shell. This is remarkable up to one year of growth (the oyster reaches maturity at two years) and in its early stages it is possible to see the beating of the heart through the shell. The shell, roughly six inches at its widest diameter, is round with one valve flat and the other slightly domed. The inner shell has a subdued pearly lustre and, being quite thin, is translucent. It is cut into diamond-shaped 'rhombic' pieces of a few square inches in area and used for glazing purposes.

From the size ranges of which the major percentages are below 1 mm and the next large group below 2 mm, it is obvious that the Placuna pearls have no commercial significance.

The pearls found in *Placenta placenta* are free pearls in the mantle. They are usually smaller than those embedded in the gonad or alimentary canal. Sometimes clusters of minute pearls are found but blisters are scarcely seen. *P. placenta* occur mostly in bays and inshore waters. They are not considered as true oysters, having no byssus in adult life. They are not found at any great depth, i.e. two to four fathoms deep, i.e. 12–24 ft.

Chapter 6

Cultured pearls

Whenever high monetary value is represented in a small, portable form such as a gem, it is almost certain that someone, somewhere, sometime, will imitate it, or make a synthetic counterpart of it, following as closely as possible the chemical composition, specific gravity, optical properties and hardness of the natural gem. By-and-large, the imitators and synthesizers have succeeded tolerably well. The public, and certain sections of the gem trade, today are not able to tell the difference between the most recent diamond simulant and real diamond. Quite often, synthetic emeralds or synthetic rubies defy the ability of the wary jeweller, who eventually resorts to a trade testing laboratory for final decision. In general, if it is possible to make a statement about synthetic gems and their detection, it is that (to the expert) the synthetic has too good a colour. In fact, it tends to look too good and is often rather larger in size than nature is wont to produce.

Although the foregoing is upon colour in gems, the same premise applies to imitation pearls and cultured pearls. Cultured-pearl necklaces are usually too well matched and graded, and offer a standard of excellence which in natural pearls would present extremely large sums of money. Certainly, the jeweller became prey to the unscrupulous when the first synthetic gems appeared.

The impact of cultured pearls on the trade

In similar manner, the legitimate pearl trade suffered the first onslaughts of the successful cultured spherical pearl. It was not the intent of the Japanese producer to defraud the pearl dealers and merchants but, as is always the case, it was the dishonest element who practised such deceits.

The Japanese cultured pearl which appeared on the market around 1922 was a very able and successful accomplishment. The cultured pearl is the culmination of man's application of his knowledge of the functional biology of oysters and mussels to produce secreted layers of nacreous coatings around a loose, spherical mother-of-pearl bead introduced into the soft parts of the body of the oyster (*see*

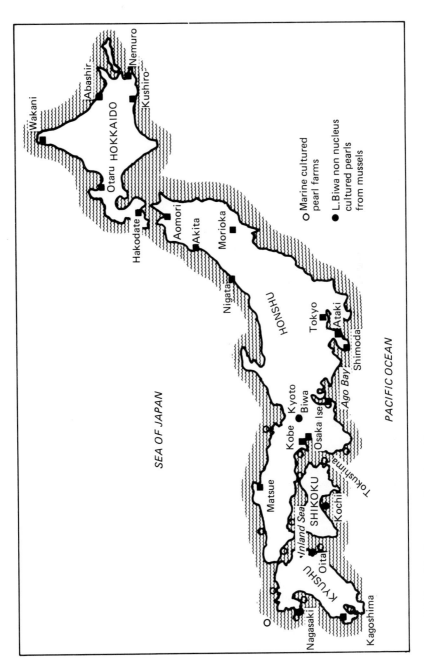

Figure 6.1 Map of the Japanese cultured pearl farms

Chapter 4, 'The structure and anatomy of the pearl oyster'). To the unaided or unskilled eye the result outwardly resembles a pearl. Because pearls are opaque, it is not possible to look into their interiors; thus the clever Japanese adapted biological functions to furnish the nucleus bead insert with an apparently natural exterior.

If one can generalize upon the characteristics of cultured pearls, it will be to say that regularity of production, even the regularity of irregularities that appear, and of regularity of tone, colour, size and grading give the hints or clues as to their provenance. It would be foolish to assume that because a 'pearl' necklace looks fine, is well matched and is beautifully graded that it is necessarily a cultured pearl necklace. There are many superb natural necklaces upon the market, some are worn by royalty – but these are the unusual and exceptional pearls.

When a pearl merchant or pearl dealer is faced with a superb-looking 'pearl' necklace he resorts to laboratory tests to ensure that he is purchasing natural pearls. Most pearl experts, auction houses and other buyers and sellers of fine quality and important pearls usually have a very shrewd knowledge and can mostly distinguish by experience natural or cultured pearls. However, when cultured spherical pearls first came upon the world markets, the legitimate trade suffered a considerable set-back, which also embraced the period of the Wall Street crash and the world slump. The mere fact that to the practised eye a pearl or pearl necklace 'looked suspicious' was not sufficient to satisfy the careful merchant. Steps were taken to devise methods which could quickly and positively identify and prove cultured pearls as well as natural pearls without danger or damage to the precious material.

Chinese cultured pearls, 1000 BC

Although from a commercial point of view cultured pearls first appeared in the early 1920s, the Chinese had used freshwater mussels to coat small objects with a pearly layer as long as 3000 years ago. Kunz and Stevenson, on pages 288–289 of *The Book of the Pearl* (1908), and Streeter, on pages 254–259 *Pearls and Pearling Life* (1886), refer to the activities of villagers in the silk-producing region of North Chihkiang, near the district city of Tehtsing. Apart from slight differences in the spelling of place names, the accounts are very similar. The 'art' of covering small objects with pearly nacreous coating was practised in or confined to two villages. In the period May to June specially-selected full-grown mussels were transported from Lake Tahu about 30 miles from Kiangsu. Following their transportation they were rested submerged in bamboo cages for several days before insertion of the nuclei. These were pellets of dried mud compounded with juice of seeds from camphor trees. Sometimes they were pellets of mother-of-pearl from pearl oysters. These were ground together in an iron mortar to produce spherical smooth surfaces – rather like the ceramic spheres used to triturate pigments in the paint industry. Other popular subjects used as nuclei were small images of Buddha which were usually in the form of very thin castings of lead.

The method

The mussel shell was opened with a mother-of-pearl spatula and the foreign bodies positioned with a forked bamboo stick to form two parallel rows between the mantle and the inner shell wall. The process was repeated on the opposite side of the mussel. The treated mussels were then placed in pools or canals, about five to six inches apart, at a depth of two to five feet, and in quantities ranging from hundreds to thousands. The mussel cemented the nuclei against the inner shell wall by means of a membraneous secretion which contained calcareous matter and finally became a nacreous secretion which coated the nucleus pellets or Buddha castings.

When the mussels were eventually fished in November, the fleshy muscular portions were removed and the pearl-coated 'pearls' were detached from the shell. Those with a mother-of-pearl nucleus were left whilst those with metallic or earthy mixture pellets had the nucleus removed and the space filled with resin or wax. The back, or portion revealed by cutting from the shell, was then covered by a skilfully worked mother-of-pearl cover. The spherical pearl pearl blisters which had to be removed from the shell were about three-quarters or more orbicular and thus, when carefully mounted, looked like whole real pearls. The Buddhas were used as dress ornamentation. Some shells were sold as curios with their attached 'pearls' and Buddhas *in situ*. A good example can be seen in the pearl display on the ground floor Gemstone Exhibition in the Geological Museum, Exhibition Road, London.

The hardy mussel

It is certainly a tribute to the physiological powers of the mussel that it can survive such operations and successfully secrete in a matter of a few months a nacreous covering over as many as twenty-five 'pearl' beads, or up to sixteen Buddhas. It is worth noting here that from the early beginnings of nuclei insertion by the Chinese, some 3000 years ago, in an area of silkworm and mulberry cultivation, to the present-day Japanese production of non-nucleated pearls, q.v., it is again the hardy freshwater mussel which seems to possess remarkable reproductive and recuperative powers. In the first examples the Chinese were said to have ultilized the pearl mussel *Mytilus cygnus* (Dr D. T. Macgowan in the *Journal of the Society of Arts*, 1853). The British Museum exhibits such shells and their included blister nuclei.

Spherical cultured pearls

It was not, however, the ingenious curios of three-quarter spherical blister pearls or pearl-coated Buddhas which caused such consternation to the legitimate pearl trade, but the introduction of cultured, whole *spherical* pearls, *not* blisters. These 'spherical pearls' were, to all intents and purposes, a serious problem at the period of the early 1920s.

The first Japanese cultured pearls

There is a little vagueness upon the actual origination of the method of producing in Japanese waters the spherical loose cultured pearl. Certainly the name Kokichi Mikimoto springs foremost to the minds of jewellers as being the father figure of the Japanese cultured pearl industry. Undoubtedly, Mikimoto put the cultured pearl upon the commercial map.

B. W. Anderson, in his *Gemstones for Everyman,* gives an intriguing description of the world's first independent pearl-testing station which he was asked to organize and operate, and states that the first *whole* cultured pearl appeared in 1921. He established the pearl-testing station in 1925 under the auspices of the Committee of the Diamond, Pearl and Precious Stone Trade Section of the London Chamber of Commerce. The production of a whole, spherical pearl was achieved by adapting the funtions of the pearl-bearing oyster.

The early workers in Japan

Mikimoto was important, not only in the original Japanese blister cultured pearls, but in the commercially successful promotion and marketing of cultured pearls. Certainly the Japanese were the prime workers in this industry. In his book *Gems,* Webster prefers as cultured pearl originator Tatsuhei Mise, a carpenter whose stepfather's journey on an oyster-prospecting trip to Australia, stimulated Mise's interest in pearls. Tatsuhei, who had no scientific training, is said to have produced a whole, cultured pearl around a lead pellet prior to 1904. The Japanese oyster *Pinctada martensi* was used for the tissue graft production. Because Mikimoto patented his process for *hemispherical* cultured pearls in 1896, Mise was not allowed a patent for his whole, spherical pearl process when he applied for a patent in 1907. There is no record extant of Mise's work, except that he was allowed to patent a needle he employed in his method.

Altogether there seems to be some uncertainty as to who really should be accorded the accolade of having first successfully produced a marketable, spherical cultured pearl. From a scientific base, as opposed to the humble attempts by Tatsuhei Mise, a technician named Tokichi Nishikawa, employed in the Japanese Bureau of Fisheries until 1905, planned to produce cultured pearls using silver and gold nuclei. Nishikawa applied for a patent on 23 October 1907, which was five months later than that of Tatsuhei Mise. The Patent Office accepted Nishikawa's application on the grounds that he had completed his invention as early as 1899. This application by Nishikawa, however, was to afford him protection for his work but it was not until 1916 that it was fully patented and Mise's early application was overhauled as an infringement. In 1908 Mise and Nishikawa signed an agreement of joint ownership of the Mise/Nishikawa method. This seemed to Webster to point to the priority of Mise's work, a tribute to the pioneering work and spirit of an unlettered man. Nishikawa died in 1909.

Once more, in 1914, Mikimoto appeared on the scene with an application for his own method to be patented. This was granted in 1916, fifty days before the Nishikawa patent which had been applied for seven years earlier. Webster points out that Mikimoto's patent was not his own work but that of his friend Otokichi Kuwabara who was a dentist by profession. The Kuwabara/Mikimoto method was to wrap a bead nucleus in tissue from the mantle of another oyster, to tie it with silk thread and press it into position in the 'mother' oyster. It proved to be too delicate and wasteful a process compared to the Mise/Nishikawa method which is used to this day in Japanese cultured pearl production. The result of intermarriage between the families involved afforded some solidarity and concerted effort, which today is seen in the organization of the workforce which operates successfully on Pearl Island, some 200 metres off-shore at Toba Bay and at Ago Bay near Shima Hanto, a peninsular forming a large portion of the Shima National Park. This is literally Mikimoto country. In the Mie Prefecture on the east coast of the main Japanese island of Honshu, Ago Bay (*Colour plate 10*) with its calm waters of even temperature is particularly well suited to the cultivation of pearl oysters, and it is extremely photogenic, the rafts moored in the bay forming an extra pictorial interest.

Kokichi Mikimoto

Mikimoto was born on 25 January 1858, the eldest son of the Mikimoto who ran a noodle shop named 'Awako' in the town of Toba in Shima. He had a rudimentary education in a one-room grade school run by Ryokya Kurihara. Reading, writing and arithmetic were his sole studies. At 14 he became a vegetable vendor, helping out family finances, but later decided to follow business in marine products – a natural choice for a man raised in a port town on the Shima peninsula. Mikimoto was attracted to the pearl industry (natural pearls). Because of high prices paid for pearls, the pearl-bearing oysters were fished regardless of supplies or continuing supplies. Only one or two pearls were found in several thousand oysters and these were not necessarily fine quality. He became interested in the protection and propagation of oysters because they represented a valuable national asset. Following on from pearl oyster protection (rather like Professor Herdman who examined the pearl oyster paars (banks) of Sri Lanka in the Gulf of Mannar), Mikimoto extended oyster protection with the artificial growing of pearls.

The first pearl farm

Mikimoto established his first pearl farm in 1888 on the Shinmei inlet in Shima, though he needed to know more about oysters; there were many problems in biology and marine science to overcome. In April 1890 he exhibited live oysters which he had grown, plus pearls and pearl products, at the 3rd Domestic Fair in Uneo Park where he met Professor Kakichi Mitsukuri of Tokyo University, an authority on marine biology. Mikimoto learned from Professor Mitsukuri the basics of nacreous secretion by oysters as a form of protection to isolate intruders (or repair shell damage). According to a brochure based upon a book titled *Kokichi Mikimoto* by Iwazo Otsutake, the comparatively young Mikimoto started his pearl-cultivating project the day after his meeting with Professor Mitsukuri.

The brochure praising Mikimoto mentions that a German named von Hessling had attempted pearl cultivation in river waters ninety years before and that no attempts had been made in England, France or America (the important pearl markets of the world). This was said to have inspired Mikimoto to follow an unexplored project – but what of Linnaeus in 1761? The Chinese, as previously described, had produced part-spherical cultured pearls from mussels 3000 years before.

Mikimoto's first attempts were made in sea-water oysters in which he implanted spherical beads of mother-of-pearl. The treated oysters were placed in bamboo baskets and moored in the sea. Natural pearls take a long time to develop. Mikimoto implanted his spheres and every few months examined his treated oysters. Most of the implants were rejected, the remainder showed no apparent change. He had converted all of his assets into oysters and was working in poverty. His wife Ume was a loyal and devoted worker with him. In 1862 a red tide caused by an excess of plankton, completely exterminated the oysters being cultivated at Bentenjima Island in the Shinmei inlet. There were some oysters left at Toba on what is now called Pearl Island.

It was on 11 July 1893 that Ume checked a bamboo basket of treated oysters as a matter of routine and found their first cultured *blister* pearl – the patent for this procedure was granted on 27 January 1896.

Following this success, Mikimoto set up in Ago Bay a pearl farm around an uninhabited island which was later named Tatokujima Island. The sudden death of his wife at the age of 32 spoiled his brief enjoyment of success but, being very strong-willed, he carried on with cultivating hemispherical cultured pearls, with the development of *whole,* spherical pearls as his objective. He suffered a second set-back in 1905 with further devastation of his pearl cultivating farm by the red tide.

With 85 000 oysters dead, Mikimoto closeted himself in his small laboratory and set about the melancholy task of opening them. To his great excitement and joy he discovered his first completely spherical, whole cultured pearl. Five such examples were found, all of which were cut through the centre to show the spherical nucleus which had been implanted. After many experiments he developed a foolproof method for which a patent was registered on 12 February 1908 (Patent No 13673). Basically, the method was to wrap a mother-of-pearl sphere in a piece of tissue from a sacrificed oyster, to tie it with a very fine silk thread, and implant it into the soft part of the body of the oyster by pressing. This technique devised by a friend of Mikimoto, was termed the 'all-lapped' method.

It was a delicate operation and somewhat wasteful – presumably because of rejection and oyster mortality. The method devised by Mise/Nishikawa is nowadays used as a basis for pearl culture, but because of his life-long work on oyster propagation, pearl cultivation and commercial promotion, it is inevitable that Mikimoto is accorded foremost place in the annals of Japanese pearl culture.

The cultivation of pearls

The undoubted popularity of pearls, the appreciation of their beauty and, of course, their monetary value, created an ever-increasing demand for them. The Romans had a greed for pearls and such a love of display that laws were passed to prevent too many people indulging this inordinate passion for them. However, various laws passed were avoided, evaded or disregarded; thus, the demand for pearls continued and placed them high in world values.

Much later, when fluctuating harvests caused uncertainty of supply – particularly of those from the Gulf of Mannar (Sri Lanka) – other sources for pearls were considered.

In 1761 Carl Linnaeus, the Swedish naturalist (1732–1795) devised a method of producing pearls which was basically to drill a fine hole in mussel shell and insert a spherical bead of marble or limestone, etc, on the end of a fine wire and seal the opening. This produced some not very exciting 'pearls'.

However, the researchers were investigating the origin of pearls and slowly the evidence and knowledge were building up. The declaration of Rondelet in 1554 that pearls were diseased concretions was followed by Anselmus de Boot's theory (1600) that pearls and shells are structually similar. The basis of this theory was agreed by the Portugese traveller, Pedro Teixeira (1608). Réaumur, the French physicist, stated in 1917 that pearls have a *concentric* structure similar to that of a shell which is *layered,* and that pearls were formed of misplaced pieces of shell covered by sections which normally produce the shell. Both Réaumur's and Linnaeus' ideas suggested that pearl formation needed a hard irritant to start secretion.

Sir Everard Home in 1826 examined the centres of nacreous pearls and found no nucleus except a bright cell centre which he presumed was an aborted ova round which secretions accumulated. The Italian naturalist Filippo de Filippi published a paper in 1852 reporting that pearls occurred in the freshwater mussels, *Anodonta cygnea,* the European 'swan mussel', which were infected with parasitic worms; remnants of trematode worms were seen as nuclei. Kuchenmeister and Mobius, in 1856 and 1857 respectively, included pearl oysters with mussels as being infested with parasitic intruders. E. F. Kelaart found in 1859 various parasitic worms and silicious skeletons of diatoms as nuclei in pearls. Raphaël Dubois in 1901 followed the findings of Garner (1871) that pearls in English mussels were due to the presence of distomid larvae. H. L. Jameson wrote the life history of the trematode worm *Distomum somateriae* and its relation to pearls in the English mussel *Mytilus.* Dubois claimed in 1903 to have mixed barren pearl oysters in the Gulf of Gabes with trematode-invested mussels and quickly produced pearls, but this claim is disputed.

Many scientists, physicists and marine biologists were now examining the parasitic-intrusion theory of the origin of pearls.

Methods of increasing pearl production

About the turn of the 19th century, when the supply of natural pearls was diminishing, it was thought that a means of stimulating pearl production would be useful and profitable. Jameson concluded in 1902 that the production of pearls could be promoted by infecting oysters with parasitic hosts. Such a wholesale method seemed attractive when compared with the treatment of individual molluscs with solid intrusions made in the manner of Carl Linnaeus.

Solid nuclei intrusions

The early production by the Chinese (13th century) of pearl-coated objects from freshwater mussels has already been described. In Japan, Kokichi Mikimoto had succeeded in 1893 in extending the method of molluscan mantle secretion to coat mother-of-pearl spheres, which, being attached to the inner nacreous lining of the shell, were *blister* cultured pearls needing to be sawn from the shell. This again was a solid single intrusion and not parasitic infestation. In 1858 von Hessling stated that pearls in the freshwater mussel, *Unio margaritifera,* were formed in an epithelial sac (cyst). Professor L. Jameson's prophecy that pearls by parasitic infestation and sac formation was not necessarily wrong, but the Japanese who were working on similar lines decided that the sac, or cyst, was the important part of the 'process'.

Cyst or sac pearls

Tokichi Nishikawa in 1907 decided that mantle tissue which had migrated into the body of the oyster propelled by a foreign body, divided and surrounded the hard irritant and formed a sac (of epithelial cells). As already noted, Tatsuhei Mise applied for a patent for the simple method of culturing *spherical* pearls by inserting a bead of nucleus of pearl shell with a piece of mantle tissue from another 'sacrificed' oyster.

By the early 20th century the method was perfected and *circa* 1921 spherical cultured pearls were successfully produced and were upon the world markets.

To Kokichi Mikimoto, however, must go the accolade of 'The Pearl King'. It was he who successfully marketed cultured pearls and put Japan in the commanding position in the industry which she still holds today. He eventually used the Mise/Nishikawa method for all his cultured pearls.

The method of pearl cultivation

Because oysters have many enemies which prey upon them, and since natural pearl production by oysters is entirely accidental and not a normal function, it follows that potential pearl-bearing oysters should be reared in safety under ideal conditions. Such a situation is revealed when one studies the Japanese pearl cultivation farms.

Spat collection

The young oysters, termed 'spat', are reared in special areas before being used for pearl cultivation. The spat is collected by hanging from rafts branches of pine trees to which young oysters cling in their early days; they are later gathered and placed in specially-prepared cages where they grow undisturbed. They are in fact a healthier crop than the originally-fished oysters which may well have been assailed by the many problems and hazards of their natural environment.

Critical temperatures

The rearing rafts and cultivation rafts are moored in calm waters where there is a gentle current which carries sufficient plankton (food) to the oysters. The temperature varies only slightly and although the range of temperatures in which the Japanese oyster is able to develop can vary from 13° to 25°C, it prefers temperatures of 23° to 25°C. 18°C is considered ideal for nucleus insertion.

Nucleus insertion

Ideally the insertions are made between late April and early July and again from mid September to late October. The practice is to insert a spherical bead of mother-of-pearl into the body of the oyster, together with a cube of mantle tissue from a second oyster. Generally the bead nucleus is from 5–7 mm in diameter but with smaller nuclei several insertions may be made into one oyster. The insertion and placing of nucleus and mantle tissue into the ventral swelling of the gonad is a skilled and delicate operation. Oysters are live and mantle-edge tissue from one needs to be transferred rapidly to the other to guarantee survival. The operators, termed 'tama-ire-san' (nucleus pushers), are regarded as the élite in the industry.

Source of nuclei

The bead is, or used to be, mainly from freshwater mussel shell from the river Mississippi. It is acceptable to the oyster, and, being lack lustre, it does not affect the eventual colour of the cultured pearl. Because of trade sanctions and Second World War embargoes, the supply of American freshwater mussel shell has decreased considerably. Today, use of Trocus shell from Singapore for nuclei is becoming commoner. One of the benefits gained by laboratory X-ray workers was that the Mississippi bead nucleus had a strong phosphorescent glow. Considerable information on the luminescent characteristics of freshwater products was derived from the researches of Dr A. E. Alexander at the Mellon Institute of Industrial Research, Pittsburgh, USA.

Operating preparations

The oysters to be operated on are prepared by forcing them to gape and inserting a wooden wedge between the valves. The operator is supplied with several oysters at a time, the number depending upon her skill. The largest oysters are inserted with the largest nuclei, and the others *pro rata*.

Sacrificed oysters

The mantle edge tissue from a separate oyster is cut as a strip about 7 cm in length which is diced into cubes of about 3 mm^3. The strip of mantle and the cubed portions of tissue are prepared on a wooden cutting block. The prepared cubes are generally one-third the size of the bead nucleus to be inserted. The wooden block and cut tissue are dipped into a container of sea-water at a temperature approximating between 17°C and 22°C. They will live, if kept moist, for up to two hours. Little mention is made of the mortality rate following the operation, or even of rejection of the nucleus, but these still are factors to be considered.

The oyster, ready prepared, with valves prised open, is kept ready and the whole operation – not the preparation – is swiftly carried out by the dextrous Japanese girls. The oyster is held on the bench in a purpose-made clamp at eye-level to the operator who uses specialized tools, among which are a scalpel, a cup-ended probe, a spatula and a retractor hook.

Speed of operation

One much-read author described the speed and dexterity of the operators as the speed of the hand deceiving the eye. Eighteen seconds was the best performance time for the insertion of tissue and bead nucleus and none was slower than 30 seconds. The operator, using a spatula, smooths the fold of the mantle to uncover the body and the foot, the latter being held down to prevent muscular reaction; a slit is cut into the foot which is then extended to the main portion of tissue. A cube of tissue is pushed along this passage, followed by the mother-of-pearl bead nucleus, which is held in a cup-shaped probe. Thus, epithelial tissue and bead nucleus are adjacent; the cut is smoothed over by the back of the scalpel, mucus aiding the scarred flesh. As the mantle fold is gently replaced the foot is released from the pressure of the retractor and the wedge is removed from the valves. The oyster is returned to culture cages for a period of four to six weeks for convalescence. There can be no visual inspection of the worker's accuracy in placing the nucleus.

The mortality rate

The mortality rate can be as much as 50 per cent. This can be a very expensive business in other areas of pearl culture, particularly with *Pinctada maxima* which can cost considerable money per shell. In an attempt to combat the mortality rate the instruments as well as the nucleus are dipped in the antibiotic aureomycin.

Growth times

The inserted epithelial tissue will start to multiply, depending upon water temperature, after about ten days and will form a sac around the bead nucleus and start to secrete and cover the intruding bead. Once the treated oysters have passed a convalescent stage thay are transferred to permanent culture rafts from which the cages are suspended at a depth of seven to ten feet. The cages are lifted about three times a year and the oysters cleaned of marine growth. An average cultured pearl takes about 3½ years to grow.

Thickness of layers

The secretion of nacre from the cells of the pearl sac forms three to four layers per day, but this can vary according to season and temperature (*Figure 6.3*).

Temperature needs to be above 15°C for layers to be produced. Medium-quality pearls are said to have a thickness of pearl surrounding the bead nucleus of 0.4 to 0.5 mm. One thousand layers could take a year, each layer being 0.5 microns in thickness. Needless to say, there are variations in the thickness of the pearl coating, the bead and the quality of the nacreous covering, depending upon the season when it was retrieved.

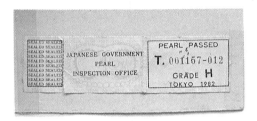

Figure 6.2 (*above*) Japanese Government quality check label, T = Tokyo (Photo: R K Mitchell)

Figure 6.3 (*right*) A very thick-skinned cultured pearl showing head nucleus, conchiolin ring and natural outer layers (Photo: B W Anderson)

The harvest

December and January are the harvesting months for cultured pearls in Japan because the flow of nacre then is of a finer quality. Usually the rafts of near-mature cultured oysters are moved to less saline waters for a month or two to improve nacre quality and are finally fished December to January.

Bleaching

The cultured pearls are extracted simply by opening the oyster and removing them, and they are then washed free from mucus and slime and finally dried. Most Japanese cultured pearls have a hint of greenish hue when first extracted; some are of a darker colour but most of this is lost very quickly by a bleaching in weak hydrogen peroxide solution.

According to one account, only about one in four oysters prepared with nuclei will produce a cultured pearl after three years, and only one in four of the these will be of marketable quality.

Size of nuclei

The Japanese oyster, *Pinctada martensi*, accepts bead nuclei of up to 6 or 7 mm, but specialized selection and breeding by the Japanese has now produced an oyster which will accept nuclei of up to 8–9 mm. This will ideally produce cultured pearls of 10 mm sizes. The largest cultured pearls raised from Japanese waters come from the warmest areas of Kyushu. The longer the period an oyster retains a nucleus bead does not necessarily infer that it will grow *pro rata* larger although it is a guide that could be accepted as a generalization. In Japanese waters the oysters sown with 6 mm nuclei yield mostly cultured pearls of 6.6 and 6.5 mm sizes and possibly some of up to 8 mm.

P. martensi and *P. radiata* are the main oysters used for pearl cultivation in Japan. The latest ruling is that *P. fucata* is not a valid species and that *P. radiata* is the correct name. Some confusion has existed over nomenclature; this is now clarified by a monograph on the *Pinctada* by a French worker, G. Ranson.

The largest pearl oysters

Cultivation of the largest of all oysters, *P. maxima,* with nuclei of 7 and 8 mm, produces after three years a range of cultured pearls with diameters from 8 mm all the way up to 16 mm. The South Seas pearl-bearing oysters furnish the largest cultured pearls and at a quicker rate than those of Japan. However, one must remember that generally the Australian natural pearl has a whiter matter colour than that of smaller oriental pearls; therefore, thicker coatings of Australian nacre will produce cultured pearls of a similar 'white' appearance.

Colour in cultured pearls

Colour in cultured pearls is governed by factors similar to those which dictate the colour in natural pearls. Salinity of the water, richness or excess of conchiolin, temperature and the health of the oyster all play a part, as does the species, i.e. silver-lip, gold-lip and black-lip types of pearl oyster.

Other cultured-pearl-producing areas

Whilst Japan remains the prime producer of good-quality, average-sized cultured pearls, other areas in warm waters are now used to rear oysters and cultivate pearls.

Australia

Australia, one of the new sources of pearls compared with Sri Lankan, Persian Gulf and Red Sea sources, was strongly against cultured-pearl production until 1956 when a trial run of three years was sanctioned by the Government of Western Australia (*Colour plate 9*). When large cultured pearls and cultured blister pearls appeared upon the market in 1958 it was a sign that a fast rate of growth was being achieved by the use of the largest of oysters, *P. maxima.*

P. maxima and *P. margaritifera* are also used in other pearl cultivation farms in Burma, Philippines, Tahiti (black-lip *P. margaritifera*); the latter black cultured pearls are very popular. In a retail shop window, not a stone's throw from Hatton Garden, the author saw a fine display of normal Japanese cultured-pearl necklaces, accurately described as such, but in the same window there were necklaces of black 'pearls' labelled as 'Pearls from Tahiti', and underneath in microscopically-small print the word 'cultured'! All cultured pearls should be described as such in letters of equal size for both 'cultured' and 'pearls'.

The Philippines

The Philippines have several pearl-cultivation farms on which the technicians are mostly Japanese. The cultured-pearl farms set up in the Philippines use the Mindanao Sea as their source of supply for *P. maxima* (nowadays there is in the Australian pearl waters an ever-diminishing supply of this largest of oysters). The cultured pearls grown in the Philippines are a very acceptable creamy colour touched with a rosée tint. Because of the strong ties with Japanese technicians, the chief market of Philippines cultured pearls is Tokyo, and not Manila, as would be expected.

The large *P. maxima* oysters are gathered in the Mindanao Sea area and flown or transported to the pearl-culture farms set up in the Philippines. Preservation of the oysters during transport, suitability for perfection in cultivation and size and age, are a few of the factors to be considered. Piracy, theft, and possible eventual rejection, plus the distance from home of the workforce, make the successful harvest, after years of growth, even more difficult to achieve.

When one reads of 'abundant' or 'inexhaustible' supplies of pearl oysters and very shortly after of a worsening shortage, and of oyster-rearing farms to ensure the continuing supply of the humble oyster which, given its freedom, breeds prolifically, one wonders at man's wastage of natural resources. We have almost swept the seas of whales, herrings are diminishing in numbers and the humble oysters are disappearing. The vast banks of discarded shells on Lake Biwa, the mounds of shells in the near-exhausted rivers of the once-prolific Mississippi basin, all signify man's desire to emulate nature – nature who disposes perfection so rarely in gems.

Problems of labour and shell supply

Closure of cultured-pearl farms

A sign of the times is brought sharply into focus with the announcement of the closing down of the world's largest cultured-pearl farms in the Torres Strait on the Thursday, Moa and Friday Islands culture farms. The news was briefly reported in Britain in the *Retail Jeweller* trade newspaper on 22 September 1983.

Further details appeared in the *Cairns Post* (north eastern Australia–Barrier Reef area). The management of Pearls Pty Ltd is reported as saying that the Torres Strait farms would close by 1985 – they had pioneered the farms in 1956. Economic and natural causes combined to make the future for the company untenable, and no amount of aid proffered by the Government of Western Australia could help them.

Reports on cultured-pearl farming in Australia

The main pearling farm, owned by Pearls Pty Ltd of Tokyo, is at Kuri Bay just south of Broome in Western Australia. The Kuri Bay project has been subsidizing the Torres Strait pearl farms but a disease at Kuri Bay, which killed off the oysters, coupled with a cyclone in March 1983, had caused considerable damage to rafts and oyster stock. The company's family name is 'Kuribayashi', hence the name 'Kuri Bay'.

Live oysters have to be transported, and this is an expensive item in a remote area. Renewal costs of luggers and shell transporters are prohibitive, the latter could be around 1.5 m Australian dollars. Transporting labour by seaplane from Broome to Kuri Bay is expensive – and people do not want to go to such distant places. As an example, if he stays in his own area a Torres Strait islander can obtain just as much money by accepting social security hand-outs and doing the odd job for cash, such as a day or two on a crayfish boat. Trouble with unions and all the attendant upsets and demands, plus competition from other areas, combined with exhaustion of sources of supply, are other problems.

A further interesting but sad note is added by the reports in the Australian newspaper *National Weekend,* July/August 1983 which describe the lot of the Japanese divers who scour the sea-bed at Eighty Mile Beach, searching for oysters. They are now unemployed and each morning fill in time in the local Japanese cemetery, a few kilometres outside Broome, where they repaint the faded characters on headstones of the graves of some 900 Japanese divers who have died of the 'bends' through searching for pearl oysters. The graves date back to 1896 when the first Japanese diver died. The same report notes that the four luggers of the company's fleet will be up for sale the following month.

Other remarks concerning the Torres Strait pearl farm also state the lower labour costs of pearl operators in other areas, especially Indonesia.

Other areas in Australia may continue to produce cultured pearls but on smaller-scale sites under individual concentrated conditions. Reports vary on the cost of oysters but figures of twelve dollars and fourteen dollars each are given by reliable sources. When one considers these prices and that the oyster has to be transported and settled ready for operating upon, following which a further wait of at least two years for a result, or even a rejection, it is not surprising to find that a firm closes down, particularly if it has had high labour costs and visitations by disease and cyclones.

In a summing up of the Kuri Bay and Torres Strait (Thursday Island, etc) closures, the following observations were made in August 1983: 'The cultured pearl industry is a very labour-intensive industry. It needs a continuous supply of oysters in *good condition.* The oysters need not necessarily be cheap provided the oyster is in good condition by the time it is ready to be operated upon. The yield and quality of such a product will be fair to good, and more than compensate for its initial cost.' The report adds further: 'The condition of the oysters at Kuri Bay and Thursday

Island is poor. Mortality rates of 60 per cent are admitted. Although the number of shells is increasing in the Thursday Island area, the mortality rate remains the same for the smaller shells with a decline as the shells grow larger.'

Another point of interest in the reports is the belief that the oysters are building up a resistance to the disease caused by contamination due to an oil spill in 1970. It suggests that a small farm could profit from the production of Mabe (*see* page 79).

Future prospects

The report quoted above concludes with the observation that prospects for pearl culture are good in Indonesia, poor in Australia. It also points out that political climates could change, and that a good insurance policy would be for potential buyers to obtain a good pearl-oyster-producing farm to fall back upon should matters cause a hold up or stop the Indonesian area's supplies. As will be gathered from the note on the vicissitudes of the Australian scene, labour and multinational complications have dogged the Australian pearl, mother-of-pearl and cultured pearl operations. Perhaps a respite from fishing, as has occurred elsewhere, may provide an opportunity for the oysters to proliferate and provide a future source for programmed farming. Perhaps a lesson, or even hope, may be drawn from the fact that in a different gem market De Beers with extra-sensory equipment carried out a detailed re-examination of their mounds of already-processed blue ground and proved it to be a profitable operation (Gemmological Conference, The Hague, 1977).

Non-nucleated cultured pearls

The heading of this section describes the new type of cultured pearl which arrived upon the market in Great Britain towards the middle/late 1950s. The Japanese had worked assiduously towards production of cultured pearls from freshwater sources, i.e. mussels. It was known, of course, that *natural* freshwater pearls had occupied a reasonably important position in pearl markets and historically were known in Great Britain by the Romans. Some say it was the pearls from the rivers of England which made the Romans desirous of occupation!

The Japanese, having succeeded in producing cultured pearls from sea-water oysters in a dramatic and economically satisfactory manner, turned their attention to freshwater mussels as a potential source. From 1911 to 1925, under the encouragement of the governor of the Shiga Prefecture, attempts at pearl culture had been made with the freshwater mussel *Cristaria plicata*. In 1924 the use of *Cristaria plicata* was discontinued and replaced by the larger mussel, *Hyriopsis schlegeli*.

Lake Biwa, the largest lake in Japan, is situated approximately ten miles north east of Kyoto and covers an area of about 180 square miles. In Lake Biwa there was an apparently inexhaustible supply of the fairly large mussel, *Hyriopsis schlegeli*

(*Colour plate 18*). This mussel, which is about 9 in (maximum) in length, lives to about 13 to 15 years and at the seven-years-old stage is ready for the culturing of pearls. It reaches maturity at ten to 13 years.

These prolific supplies of the mussel *Hyriopsis schlegeli* are collected by trawling the lake bed with rakes which have suitably-sized gaps between the prongs to prevent small mussels being fished. This is to conserve stocks but already the pearl cultivators are growing new supplies of mussels in specially-designated areas.

At first when nuclei were inserted into the mussel, the lack of space available – due to the coiled intestine of the animal – caused a high percentage of deaths and poorly-coloured 'pearls'. Later, it was found that by eliminating the solid nucleii and inserting pieces of mantle tissue (epithelium) into the gonads (sex organs) of the mussel – simply by pressing them into position – several rather poorly-coloured baroque 'pearls' were produced. Further experimentation found that considerable improvement in shape and colour were obtained if the diced (cube-shaped) pieces of mantle tissue from a donor mussel were inserted into slits/incisions made in the edge of the mantle of the producing mussel.

There are varying statements upon the crop production from mussels. At first, there were many rejects and a high mortality rate. Later, figures of successful operations mention ten incisions on each side of the mussel interior and some of twenty each side. This, of course, limits the size of cultured pearl produced.

Common sense and experimentation by the Japanese has led to a programme which produces large quantities of medium size and quality, slightly baroque, cultured pearls. They have also demonstrated that they can produce good-quality round cultured pearls of size and colour. Some extremely intriguing shapes, such as cubes, triangles, cruciform, and even 'dragons teeth', are also produced (*Colour plate 21*). The Japanese are the pioneers in this field of fancy shapes and, so far, are alone in using hypodermic syringes, air pumps and 'medicine' in their operations. Colours can now be controlled by judicious selection from certain portions of mantle tissue, together with precise positioning within the incised mantle. So confident are the Japanese of production that they issue a chart showing current shapes available (*Colour plate 22*). It is noteworthy that they are remiss in not boldly describing their products on the heading as 'cultured' in letters equal in size to the word 'pearls'. This could be misleading even though one accepts that Japanese products are cultured.

Equally impressive are the published details of non-nucleated cultured pearl production from mussels, together with the production figures of cultured pearl (bead nucleus) from sea-water oysters.

The mussel *Hyriopsis schlegeli* is unusual in its profitable production rate. Out of the total number of mussels operated upon, at least 60 per cent are successful and of the successful ones, practically 100 per cent produced their full complement of ten to 20 and up to 40 cultured pearls per mussel. This makes the standard cultured pearl with bead nucleus quite a different proposition, but there is no comparison in orient between the lesser lustre of the freshwater cultured pearl and that of the sea-water cultured oyster. Not only does the freshwater mussel in its successful yield produce 100 per cent results, but, following on the harvesting of the crop, if the mussels are returned to the water, a second crop and sometimes a third crop can be harvested. Obviously, the second crop is duller and flatter generally than the first, whilst the third crop is rather like flat slices of pearl and, not being very attractive, is sometimes ground up for 'medicine' or used as tomb pearls.

Although the Japanese were the pioneers in the production of non-nucleated cultured pearl from freshwater sources, it is said that China is fast becoming a quantity producer but not of the quality of the Japanese product. According to personal communication received, the Chinese production is haphazard in commerce and method but, despite this, their production of non-nucleated cultured pearls is in tonnes, of which 80 per cent is rice-shaped with only a small percentage free from wrinkles. The same source states that in the manufacture of gold-filled chains the raw material used as a filler is Chinese freshwater, non-nucleated, poor-quality cultured pearl. Thus we see the difference in the quality and quantity of the material produced by the Japanese and the Chinese.

When the Japanese skilfully accomplished the production of spherical cultured pearls in commercially and economically profitable numbers, they then turned their attention from the then relatively small oyster, *Pinctada martensi,* to the much larger oyster found in South Seas, and in the oysters of the north and north west coast of Australia, namely, *Pinctada maxima.* This is the largest of the pearl-producing oysters. Here again they succeeded and produced some very large fine expensive, thick-skinned cultured pearls (*Figure 6.4*). Precise figures are not available but it is no secret that the expertise of the Japanese dominated the Australian scene. After the Second World War the Japanese were absent from Australia and the trade diminished. Now an accord exists and limited numbers of skilled Japanese work with a multi-racial assortment of pearl workers. The large

Figure 6.4 A radiograph of a slightly baroque thick-skinned Australian cultured pearl showing a strong conchiolin demarcation at bead (Photo: A E Farn)

results from large oysters represent large prices, and so, stemming from their advances from *P. martensi* to *P. maxima,* the Japanese have now moved from non-nucleated cultured pearls from freshwater mussels to non-nucleated cultured pearls from sea-water oysters. This is a tremendous step which confronts the laboratory with a serious problem of identification. The identification of non-nucleated *freshwater* cultured pearls was facilitated by the characteristics of fluorescence and phosphorescence under X-ray excitation, particularly the prolonged phosphorescence and the distinctive hue of the fluorescent colour. This does not apply to sea-water oyster products which do not fluoresce.

The advent of non-nucleated cultured pearl production can only add to the problems faced by would-be purchasers of natural pearls. In the baroques, and sometimes the button shapes, produced by the non-nucleation method, it is often impossible to distinguish them from their natural counterparts when they are carefully 'salted' into lots of natural pearls. It is only when large consignments are radiographed to reveal their overall similarities of vermiform embryo centres that positive identification can be made.

It is necessary, therefore, to revert to radiography for sea-water, non-nucleated cultured pearls rather than Laue diffraction pattern work. The pearl worker/ radiographer in a gem-testing laboratory now needs to fall back upon his records, photographs and experience when interpreting radiographs which 'look' natural. The rôle played by local dentists in producing radiographs of pearls for keen-minded jewellers or gemmologists is dangerous except in the case of mother-of-pearl nucleus cultured pearls. These latter are really very easy since their large nuclei with conchiolin-ring surround occurring in practically 100 per cent of all beads of a necklace ensures that even a poor radiograph will show some signs of cultivation. If only 50 per cent show signs of cultured pearls this is a sample sufficient to be a guide.

The interpretation of radiographs of sea-water, non-nucleated, cultured pearls, usually of a size representing a potentially large sum of money, is a very responsible undertaking. The conscientious gemmologist who, by his experience, has so many possibilities and permutations to consider, is hoist by his own petard of experience.

Some difficulty is being experienced with the satisfactory impregnation of *P. maxima* as a source for non-nucleated cultured pearls. However, having seen the results of Japanese persistence and patience, it will not be surprising to find that such products have passed through the present defences. When the past results of international researches in combating the then new threats to the existing pearl trade by the nucleated cultured pearl are considered, it is hoped that a solution can be found to the problems presented by the non-nucleated cultured pearl from sea-water sources. The earlier methods were based upon the concentric and radial structure of natural pearl and the banded structure of the nucleus in cultured pearl. It seems that the lines to follow now will be emphasis on radiographic comparison with known natural photographs plus, possibly, luminescent effects and even specific gravity. It is not an insuperable position at present but it does present a problem. Similar problems occur today in the ruby, sapphire and emerald realms; they, too, are being tackled by physicists and international gemmologists.

Mabe cultured pearls, cultured blister pearls and keshi

The largest of the pearl-producing oysters, *Pinctada maxima,* was originally commercially fished for its value as mother-of-pearl shell and pearls accidentally found were considered a bonus. Such was the position just over a hundred years ago in Northern Australian waters, as has been described in the section on the Australian pearl fisheries.

Mabe cultured pearls

Today in the pearl and cultured pearl trade we have 'Mabe cultured pearls', and to purists this may be anathema because certain oysters are known to the Japanese as 'Mabe oysters'. The Mabe oyster is the black-winged pearl oyster, *Pteria penguin* which is found in the waters of Amami–Oshima, Hong Kong, Wai–Wain, Malaysia, Indonesia, Thailand and Kampuchea. The Japanese are the most successful in culturing half pearls or blisters in these oysters. The Mabe oyster, the black-winged pearl oyster, *P. penguin,* has one flat and one concave-shaped shell; hence its shape is distinctive, indeed it is not dissimilar to that of the modern 'Mabe' cultured blister pearl. To increase confusion, it must be remembered that the trade generalized its terms or descriptions in earlier days by describing most half or blister cultured pearls as 'Mabe pearls' (*Figure 6.5*). Today the Blue Book of CIBJO nomenclature and trade description under Article 17, Rules of Application, and Materials Definition B2.2 states that what used to come under 'Mabe cultured blister', etc, is now described as 'composite cultured pearl' as follows: 'Composite cultured pearls are products resulting from man's assemblage of an upper portion of cultured pearl and one or more lower portions of the same or another substance' (e.g. Mabe composite cultured pearl).

Figure 6.5 Mabe cultured blister pearl with steatite hemisphere nucleus
(Photo: R K Mitchell)

One might well ask why people go to such lengths to produce these Mabe cultured pearls. Indeed, when some of the skilled processes involved are described, it does seem puzzling in these days of high-priced labour. It is the costing and/or loss-making involved in pearl cultivation which has ecouraged the production of these large Mabe cultured blister pearls.

The pearl-bearing oyster, *P. maxima,* fished in Australian waters, is very large and becoming more difficult to find in easy depths. During cultivation of large nucleus pearls in this very large and expensive oyster, rejection of the bead nucleus often takes place. This represents a loss in time since rejection is not immediately discovered. The nacreous shell lining is no longer smooth and useful due to the corrugations caused by the oysters' reaction. The shell is unsaleable as such. If inflation (financial) is added, there rapidly accumulates a considerable loss-maker in spoiled shells.

When an oyster has rejected a whole spherical bead nucleus, it is found that it will 'accommodate' a hemispherical bead, and this is placed between the mantle and the nacreous layer. Sometimes more than one hemisphere is applied to each valve (shell), in which case they are not of mother-of-pearl but of steatite (soapstone), a very soft stone which is used because it offers no adherence or affinity to the nacreous secretions. In due course the hemispheres are covered and cemented to the inner nacreous wall of the oyster from where they are cut from the shell together with a flat parallel flange of shell adhering. They are sent to Japan to be processed. There they have the soapstone hemisphere removed and the inside of the *now* hollow blister is cleaned and bleached. The flange is removed by sawing and the hollow interior is filled with a resinous compound and/or a cylinder of mother-of-pearl plus the resinous compound. The exposed under-portion is sealed with a mother-of-pearl disc and the perimeter of joining is carefully polished. The result is an important symmetrical cultured pearl blister, looking like a large pearl, particularly if it is suitably mounted. If the back of the cultured blister is concealed by clever mounting, the result is most impressive.

The reason for all this work is simply that the high cost incurred in the loss of potential mother-of-pearl shell by rejection spoiling, plus the cost in time and labour, can be offset by the subsequent sale of these composite cultured blister pearls. They are still termed by some 'Mabe pearls'.

In an interesting aside upon this subject, Jean Taburiaux wrote in *La Perle et Ses Secretes* (1983), 'The Japanese, the Australians, and more recently the Tahitians, are currently using this technique. But we should say "re-using" this technique because do not let us forget that its invention is attributed to the Chinese in the 13th century.'

In a personal communication from a source in Japan it was stated: '*Pinctada maxima,* having once been injected with a whole round (*invariably* round) nucleus, will not retain a second nucleus after the oyster rejects the first; such oysters are generally used for making "Mabe half-pearls". However, oysters in which no nucleus has ever been inserted, will also be used for Mabe cultivation if such oysters are judged inferior and unsuitable for producing whole pearls; the same could also apply to oysters too old for round pearl production. Some farms, especially those operated by less skilled technicians and, more especially, farms run by local Australian white labour, will make only Mabe and not attempt to produce a whole pearl; such farms flourish only when Mabes can command high prices internationally.'

Cultured blister pearls

Confusion can occur when trying accurately to describe the Mabe cultured blister pearl. The earlier trade custom of terming most half or blister cultured pearls as 'Mabe pearls', and the use of the word 'Mabe' by the Japanese for a definite type of oyster, can be muddling. It is not too difficult simply to describe as cultured blister pearls, *not* Mabe cultured pearls, those which have a mother-of-pearl nucleus still retained, having never been separated. Usually these cultured blister pearls are nearly three-quarter spheres or hemispherical in shape and have a sawn-off base, exposing nucleus and nacreous skin. The Mabe cultured blister pearl has had its steatite hemispherical nucleus removed and replaced by a filler of resin plus possibly a plug of mother-of-pearl, and its base covered by a carefully fitted and polished mother-of-pearl disc.

Keshi

The word 'keshi' is a Japanese word meaning the smallest particle imaginable, e.g. a grain of sand, poppy seed, etc. In the Japanese pearl business it is slang for the by-product of any oyster seeded for culturing. It is not in itself natural, being caused by the act of operating. In Japan, the act of inserting a nucleus with its attendant 'mantle piece' (epithelial tissue) into *Pinctada martensi* can cause keshi formation. This, although not naturally 'accidental' has been termed 'adventitious'.

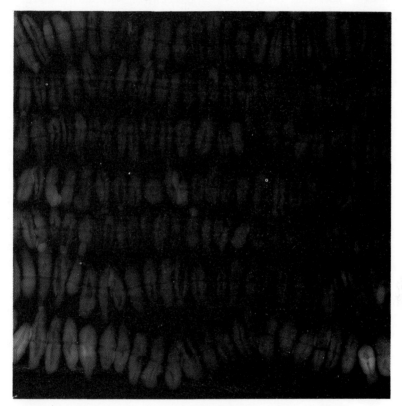

Figure 6.6 Small poor-quality non-nucleated cultured pearls from Lake Biwa, sometimes called 'keshi' (Photo: A E Farn)

With the insertion of a nucleus into the gonads, the incision itself, plus the piece of mantle tissue inserted, can cause the formation of small cysts or sacs producing small pearly baroque 'pearls', varying from 1 to 4 mm (*Figure 6.6*).

A report from a well-informed source in Japan runs as follows:

The word 'keshi' is Japanese and means 'poppy seed', it has long been used to describe in Japan a by-product of the culturing of pearl from akoya oysters; and hence has loosely also been used, perhaps mainly in Japanese, to describe all non-nucleated pearls produced, either as a result of culture or else deliberately as opposed to being a natural product.

Akoya oysters (*P. martensi*); silver-lipped or golden-lipped (*P. maxima*); black-lipped (*P. margartifera*); black-winged pearl oysters (*Pteria penguin*) are all used in various parts of the world's oceans to produce in *sea-water* whole or half pearls by the technique usually known as 'pearl culture'. This surgery on the flesh of the animal causes it to produce within organs, other than its pearl sac, tiny and small pieces of pearl apart from the prime cultured pearl; this product is generally known as 'keshi' and consists of (usually) baroque-shaped small sizes of solid pearl, though in larger sizes there may be a hollow at the centre. Without the culture operation the animal would not produce more than a small percentage of the pearl material that it has to yield when irritated by culture.

Keshi, being pure pearl, responds favourably to bleaching and treatment; and finished pearls are often lustrous, bright, white and attractive. A very small amount of akoya keshi comes in round shapes and this is sorted out in India, mixed with Persian Gulf products and sold frequently in the USA for the add-a-pearl trade. *P. maxima* of various lip colours gives also a 'keshi' of sizes larger than akoya in rough proportion to the sizes of oyster, akoya – *P. maxima*. Golden-lip shell yields a creamy-tone keshi, black-lip a grey-tone keshi. Larger sizes are doubtless sold either by ignorance, or intent, as *perles fines* and there must be pearls on which detection even by X-rays can be difficult.

Freshwater keshi
In Lake Biwa, Japan, and in river areas in China, there is a regular production of keshi pearl. In Japan the animal is a mussel, *Hyriopsis schlegeli,* and in China it is presumed that a similar mussel is employed. In Japan, and it is assumed that the Chinese copy the Japanese, small pieces of flesh are inserted into the animal, with the result that for the first year crop good quality Biwa keshi is produced; this is taken out of the mussel without the host being killed, so a second and then a third crop is also produced by the same animal without more flesh being inserted. Injections by syringe of glucose or vitamins are sometimes made but this is not universal. The second crop is duller and flatter than the first; whilst the third year crop is very thin, even like slices of pearl, lustreless and dirty and it is often used for grinding into medicine. It is not sure that the Chinese produce second and third year crops since their first year original crop is very much inferior to that of Lake Biwa, being wrinkle-skinned, dull of lustre and with many bone-like or dead pearls.

The Japanese only (not the Chinese) also pump air into the mussels' pearl sacs in order to produce within these sacs long stick-shaped pearls resembling old-time Mississippi 'dogs' teeth'; being very adept, they also can make variations of this stick shape so that the mussel produces such sticks formed either as a triangle or even cross-shaped (cruciform). By combinations of flesh and air pump, fancy shapes of keshi are also made, such as flats, ovals, and even squares.

Salt-water akoya keshi production may annually reach a weight of 400 kg; Australian keshi will, however, be only some 7 per cent of this figure. Lake Biwa production is about ten times that of akoya whilst the Chinese crop is believed to exceed greatly that of Lake Biwa. The huge majority of fresh-water keshi is made into uniform strands which are then treated into many different colours. They sell easily world-wide but especially in Western Germany.

Colour in pearls and cultured pearls

Generally speaking, buyers in European countries and most of North America prefer pearls which have basically a whitish colour with a very subtle rosée tint. Strong colours are not so popular but are used as contrasts. Naturally-coloured black, bronze and metallic-hued pearls are mounted in brooches and rings rather than being strung as necklaces.

Natural colours in pearls are due to various causes. Sometimes a pearl which has started with a conchiolin-rich centre will be affected by the domination of a dark beginning right through its layers which themselves may be white and nacreous, but to the eye the pearl will have a heavy tone of cream or appear brownish. Similarly, if a growth cycle is interrupted and a dormant non-nacreous-forming period occurs, a subsequent restart layer may be of conchiolin followed by nacreous secretion, yet giving an immediate darkening near to the surface.

Organic pigments in nacre can produce yellow and black pearls. Oysters described as 'silver-lip' or 'gold-lip' produce pearls of comparable hues, and in Tahiti naturally-coloured black *cultured* pearls are produced from *Pinctada margarifitera* black-lip oysters. The black-lip oyster succeeds best in tropical waters within a temperature range of 24° to 29°C, i.e. as in the Indian and Pacific Oceans. On Tuamotu atolls Japanese technicians assist in the delicate task of nucleus insertions. Some 'blue' pearls, which are closer to a dull leaden colour, are probably the result of a conchiolin-rich centre sometimes termed a 'mud' centre'. Radiographs will often indicate this centre structure. Yellow pearls come from gold-lip oysters whilst pearls from the large *P. maxima* silver-lip oysters are a dense white colour, lacking the subtlety of a rosée pearl from the Persian Gulf or the Gulf of Mannar. Attractive gold-coloured pearls are fished in Shark Bay on the west coast of Australia; these occur in a smaller oyster, *P. cachariarum.*

Venezuela produces pearls from *P. radiata,* an oyster about the same size as that of the Gulf of Manaar. In the laboratory Venezuelan pearls are noted for their glass-like appearance, having a degree of transparency not usually seen in other pearls. Venezuela also produces bronze- and black-coloured pearls. The glassy appearance and transparency factor is particularly noted when testing drilled pearls by the endoscope method.

Organic pigments in nacre must emanate from mantle epithelium; thus silver-lip, gold-lip and black-lip pearl oysters produce these colours in the pearls they produce. The most prominent characteristic of 'colour' in pearls is that which is described as the 'orient of pearl'. This beautiful iridescent effect is the culmination and combination of reflection, refraction and interference effects. The surface of natural pearl and cultured pearl is composed of submicroscopically thin overlapping layers of aragonite crystals of a thickness between 0.3 to 0.5 microns. Light striking the layers suffers an interference effect due to reflection from both the front and the back of these fine films. The quality or tone of this play of colour is governed to a certain extent by the distances between layer edges and the regularity of the spacings.

The orient of natural sea-water pearls from oysters is finer than that of the more subdued orient seen in freshwater pearls. Pearls from the Persian Gulf and the Gulf of Mannar have an orient far superior to that of Australian pearls. This may well be a factor of slower growth rate in the Gulf pearls as compared to that of the Australian pearl. Similarly, freshwater pearls have a coarser quality, probably because of their faster growth rate.

The part played in natural colours in pearls which stems from the mantle also governs quite strongly the colours produced in freshwater, non-nucleated cultured pearls. These are now obtainable in a wide range of colours which are not due to dyeing or bleaching but by judicious placing of the mantle tissue which itself has been purposely selected from positions in the sacrificed mussel and equally positioned in the treated mussel. In a communication received on the subject of Lake Biwa non-nucleated cultured pearls, it was indicated that local pearl fishers assert that the male shell of *Hyriopsis schlegeli* is the 'pearl' producer when fed inserts of tissue from the female shell. It is also stated that the shell with the flanged hinge is the male shell. The author, on a brief visit to Lake Biwa, was shown the smaller mussel *Anodonta,* the shell of which when held up to the light reveals subtle shades of colour in a banded arrangement. It is said that tissue taken from the *Anodonta* mantle adjacent to a position of a particular colour would, when inserted into *Hyriopsis schlegeli,* reproduce that particular colour.

Whilst strong and distinct colours other than 'white' are not usual in pearls – rather they are shades or nuances of colour – there are examples termed 'Pink Pearls' which are found in the huge conch *Strombus gigas.* The pearls are non-nacreous, having no orient, but with a structure seen at the surface which has been described as 'flame structure' or likened to the effect of watered silk, or even to silk, seen in some sapphires. An example of a fine Pink Pearl structure of good definition is shown in *Colour plate 2.*

It should be noted that under CIBJO definition rules the term 'Pink Pearls' when written must have capital initial letters in order to distinguish them from pink-hued pearls of nacreous origin (*see* Materials Definition A.2.1, Article 16, and Summary II, 'Natural Organic Substances Describing Pearl').

Strombus gigas is to be found in the Bahamas and the West Indies, on the Florida coasts and in the Gulf of California.

Lesser shades of pink and matt non-nacreous white are seen in pearls from the giant clam *Tridacna gigas* from the Indian Ocean and other tropical seas. The two shells of this clam have been known to weigh several hundred pounds the pair, and they are used as garden ornaments and especially as fonts for holy water.

The extremely rare black pearl is usually a sort of bluish black with an orient difficult to describe other than as beautiful. The finest examples are said to come from the Tuamotu Archipelago (the Pearl Islands) in the central Pacific Ocean.

Cultured-pearl production

The siting of a pearl cultivation farm has to be carefully considered from a variety of aspects and particular reasons. Protection is needed from the effects of storms, high winds and strong currents. The depth and constant temperature of the water are very important, as also is the nature of the sea-bed. The salinity of the water is equally important since this can have a marked effect upon the eventual colour of the cultured pearls. Food and oxygen need to be propelled in a smooth, lightly-moving current.

The rafts of a cultured pearl farm afford a safe and reliable setting for oyster survival and growth. Here they are protected from their natural enemies and from the effects of movement of the ocean bed which often cause the devastation of naturally-occurring paars and loss of culch.

When *P. margaritifera* and *P. maxima* are used to produce cultured pearls the oysters are submerged after successful implantation of the bead nucleus to depths ranging from 15 to 30 metres. This not only discourages theft of the valuable oysters but it also provides a non-fluctuating temperature with little change in current flow.

There is a tremendous outlay of money on equipment and for labour and skill, and there is a fairly long waiting period for the eventual harvest. All the facets are reflected in the apparently high prices demanded for fine-quality, large, symmetrically-round cultured pearls. Equally, they are reflected in the higher prices for natural pearls which have the added attribute of rarity.

There are obviously no gold-rush situations in cultured-pearl farming, and no great fortunes to be either easily or quickly made.

Production figures

TABLE 6.1. Japanese production figures for nucleated and non-nucleated cultured pearls (courtesy of the Japanese Pearl Exporters Association)

Year	Weight in momme	Value in US dollars	Value in Japanese yen
1980			
Salt-water	9 291 649	220 610 493	50 940 673 356
Freshwater	3 666 200	45 240 429	
1981			
Salt-water	8 749 998	243 810 370	53 250 987 691
Freshwater	3 114 016	37 842 082	
1982			
Salt-water	9 385 920	208 090 968	50 908 845 218
Freshwater	2 946 004	26 914 289	
1983			
Salt-water	16 684 687	284 341 037	
Freshwater	4 284 671	33 155 921	
1984			
Salt-water	19 082 583	347 928 733	
Freshwater	6 292 624	39 281 272	

NOTE: 1 momme = 3.75 grams = 18.75 carats = 75 pearl grains. Exchange rate of yen to the dollar varies from year to year.

These production figures for nucleated and non-nucleated cultured pearls, together with the export figures to various countries (*Tables 6.1* and *6.2*), were supplied by courtesy of the Japan Pearl Exporters Association, Kobe, Japan. Interesting analysis of the figures can be made which reflect widely-varying prices per momme according to quality.

When cultured pearls first came upon world markets a law was passed prohibiting their import into the Persian Gulf and associated states, and it became a serious crime to be caught in possession of them. From the export figures submitted, Saudi Arabia has now imported them (probably non-nucleated cultured) in 1981 and 1982. In 1982 the author was shown a parcel of undrilled pearls said to be Persian Gulf pearls, but which were undoubtedly non-nucleated cultured pearls.

TABLE 6.2. Export figures and values to various countries

| | 1980 | | 1981 | | 1982 | |
	Momme	*Dollars*	*Momme*	*Dollars*	*Momme*	*Dollars*
USA	175 631	3 701 050	220 531	4 318 368	249 488	4 082 133
Germany	153 185	2 275 442	117 609	1 615 147	141 498	1 640 196
Switzerland	95 605	2 444 322	62 902	1 414 173	71 817	1 031 813
Hong Kong	69 577	2 587 429	59 286	2 153 629	82 226	1 857 937
India	74 357	276 164	54 608	312 048	84 459	389 511
Spain	13 889	314 622	30 886	507 755	41 386	510 445
France	4 643	173 647	17 984	523 302	11 257	273 567
UK	3 891	75 317	14 073	326 194	12 141	219 087
Italy	15 269	355 857	13 632	134 477	7 657	82 390
Saudi Arabia	—	—	9 592	130 270	9 635	109 819
Canada	6 961	153 375	5 602	83 567	5 520	101 888
Austria	2 915	33 233	5 260	50 701	4 353	47 640
Belgium	1 053	46 927	1 229	24 998	2 288	36 456
Others	59 571	1 199 970	136 753	1 411 488	79 935	1 095 992

Among the 'others' quoted in the export figures, Lebanon must be reasonably important since it is reported that Lebanese and Indian traders would visit Japan to purchase large non-nucleated cultured pearls from Lake Biwa.

Plate 1 Natural pearls strung in sizes on silver tassels, a Bombay bunch (Photo: E Emms)

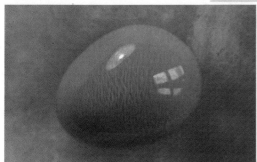

Plate 2 Flame structure of pink pearl (Photo: R K Mitchell)

Plate 3 Mabe cultured blister pearls cut from shell but not processed (Photo: B. Norman)

Plate 4 Mixed labour force gathering oyster cages
(Photo: B. Norman)

Plate 5 Some of the crop

Plate 6 Preparing an export shipment
(Photo: B. Norman)

Plate 7 Opening the oyster shells

Plate 8 Preliminary examination and descaling of
oyster shell exteriors (Photo: B. Norman)

Plate 9 An Australian cultured pearl farm (Photo: B. Norman)

Plate 10 Rafts in Ago Bay, Japan (Photo: A. Jobbins)

Plate 11 Girls working on cultured-pearl growing rafts (Photo: JPEA)

Plate 12 Cutting tissue strip from mantle (Photo: JPEA)

Plate 13 Cutting cubes from tissue strip (Photo: JPEA)

Plate 14 Workbench, oysters, beads, blocks and cubes (Photo: A. Jobbins)

Plate 15 Wedges and wedged oysters ready for insertion (Photo: A. Jobbins)

Plate 16 Inserting the mother-of-pearl bead/nucleus (Photo: JPEA)

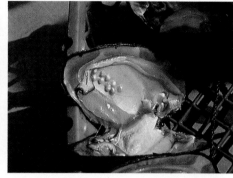

Plate 17 (*above, left*) Removing the cultured pearl

Plate 18 (*above, right*) Non-nucleated cultured pearls in *Hyriopsis schlegeli* from Lake Biwa

Plate 19 (*left*) Stringing necklaces of cultured pearls on Mikimoto's Pearl Island (Photo: A. Jobbins)

Plate 20 Fancy shapes and colours in non-nucleated cultured pearls (Photo: A Jobbins)

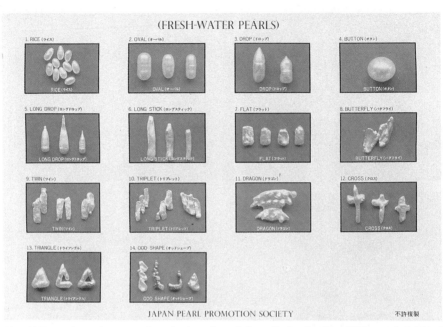

Plate 21 Fancy shapes in non-nucleated cultured pearls from *Hyriopsis schlegeli* (Photo: A. Jobbins)

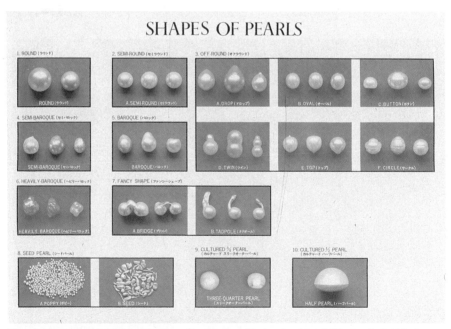

Plate 22 Shapes in non-nucleated cultured pearls from *Hyriopsis schlegeli* (Photo: A. Jobbins)

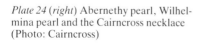

Plate 23 (*above*) The Nina Dyer necklace, three rows of black pearls (49, 49 and 53 pearls), sold in 1969 for £70000. The ear clips were sold for about £30000 (Photo: Christie's)

Plate 24 (*right*) Abernethy pearl, Wilhelmina pearl and the Cairncross necklace (Photo: Cairncross)

Plate 25 Multi-coloured pearl necklace

Chapter 7

Testing pearls and cultured pearls

Until the arrival of cultured pearls on the world market in the early 1920s, pearl merchants were engaged solely upon buying, matching, grading and selling pearls. The pearl markets of the world were centred chiefly in European capitals, important American cities and the Far East. Enormous amounts of money were spent on fine 'oriental pearls'. On the other hand, freshwater mussel pearls from rivers and lakes, though possessing a beauty distinctly their own, have never enjoyed such esteem or commanded such high prices as do oriental pearls from sea-water oysters.

Certainly, imitation pearls existed before the 1920s, some being very fine quality products, mainly hollow glass beads with an inner lustrous lining; or they were solid glass beads covered with several coats of a lacquer which contained scales taken from the bleak, a small fish caught in the river Seine in France. This fish-scale lacquer was termed *'essence d'orient'*.

Simple test methods

The stamp test

Jewellers and pearl merchants of old had *no* difficulty in detecting these imitation pearls. Pearls, in those days, were in considerable use in jewellery, small pearls particularly were applied in the embroidery of dresses, and men wore pearl dress studs and pearl stick pins. It was said that in high society, on the morning following active formation dances, quite a few loose pearls would ,be found upon the ballroom floor. Footmen would stamp upon them and those which were crushed would be the imitation pearls. Natural pearls, although comparatively soft, have a compact structure which would resist such a blow.

The bounce test

Laboratory practice would not resort to stamping on pearls as a means of distinguishing between natural, cultured and imitation pearls. However, an interesting aside on laboratory practice, and a useful tip, is that due to the very fine and regular structure of natural pearls, they bounce far more rhythmically than do cultured pearls. Because of their banded, layered structure, as distinct from the concentric regularity of natural pearls, cultured pearls have a rapidly-diminishing rate of bounce which ends in a flat thud.

The tooth test

Imitation pearls, whether hollow glass beads, wax-filled glass-beads, solid-coated glass-beads or plastics beads, are easily detected by the feel of their surface when tried against the teeth. Imitation pearls have a very smooth feel when so tested, whereas both natural and cultured pearls have a gritty pull when drawn across the teeth. This drag is due to the myriad fine edges of overlapping layers of nacreous aragonite acting in an abrasive manner against the enamel of the tooth. This is not an elegant-sounding test but one which is readily accepted as an open sesame to the pearl-dealing world.

This kind of generalized test is seized upon by some people as an easy and infallible test between real and imitation pearls, with consequent dismay when the 'real' pearls prove to be cultured. Because of their outer skin of nacreous deposits on the bead nucleus, the cultured pearl has a 'feel' similar to that of natural pearl.

Cultured half-blister pearls

The real problems came to the pearl merchants and jewellers when the first *spherical* cultured pearls came upon the market *circa* 1921. Already there were cultured half-pearls; these were usually cultured blister pearls which had developed upon the internal shell lining of the oyster as a blister. When these were sawn from the shell, their interior was exposed. Early workers termed these cultured half-pearls 'Japanese pearls' since Japan was the source. Their character was quite obvious and easy to see or detect.

Spherical cultured pearls

The next step was the triumph of Kokichi Mikimoto in producing a spherical pearl. This was unattached to the shell lining, and because its exterior was in fact 'pearl' and opaque, it presented a very real problem even to the experienced pearl merchants.

These shrewd buyers, keen judges of colour, capable of matching and grading pearls for necklaces, had considerable knowledge of their goods, gained in the hard school of buying and selling. Now they were faced with goods that experience and instincts told them were suspicious, but they could not substantiate these suspicions.

This undermining of trade confidence, added to the feeling of dealing with an unknown, had a disastrous effect upon the 'legitimate' pearl market. Merchants stopped buying and prices dropped. As shrewd merchants and business men they realized that something more than just 'suspicions of goods' would suffice – something had to be done!

The challenge of the cultured pearl

The important pearl-trading centres of the world, London, Paris and New York, were currently investigating methods and ideas for detecting cultured pearls and proving natural pearls. Workers in different countries applied themselves to the problem, using the structure of natural pearls and the composition of cultured pearls as bases for their investigations. Using the directional properties of natural pearls, i.e. their radial and concentric structure, workers devised various tests, among which were magnetic tests, optical tests and tests by X-rays using radiographs and lauegrams (diffraction patterns). Considerable ingenuity was used until ultimately methods and machines were devised which made possible positive identification in a non-destructive manner.

Although much work and discussion and differences of opinion concerning the 'origin' of pearls existed among authorities, it was generally agreed that pearls, whether from freshwater mussels or marine oysters, were basically crystalline calcium carbonate held in a framework of organic chonchiolin, the pearls having a radial and concentric structure, the radiating crystals being largely aragonite, the labile form of calcium carbonate.

Chemical tests

Considerable ingenuity was shown, particularly by French workers, in attempting to investigate the structural differences between natural and cultured pearls. Their opacity and possession of a beautiful iridescent surface presented a difficult task since they were fairly soft, although compact, non-destructive tests were essential because of their valuable nature.

Chemically, pearls and cultured pearls were calcium carbonate, chiefly aragonite, with possibly 4 per cent conchiolin and trace elements. One of the latter, manganese, was found to be more evident in freshwater pearls than it was in marine pearls – this became an important factor in ancillary tests.

The mother-of-pearl bead nucleus, originally used by the Japanese, came from the dull lack-lustre shell of Mississippi mussels. The freshwater source is also fairly strong in trace element manganese. Fortunately for the laboratory pearl tester who uses X-rays for testing pearls, it is known that whereas marine pearls are inert under X-ray excitation, X-ray fluorescence of cultured pearls, is quite strong because of the freshwater nucleus from the Mississippi mussel. Natural freshwater pearls also fluoresce.

However, when cultured pearls are examined for fluorescence, laboratory practice is to place them extremely close to the beryllium window of the X-ray tube where the glow of fluorescence would be limited to the target area, whereas a natural freshwater pearl would glow in its entirety because of its homogeneous structure. This test for fluorescence by a manganese trace in cultured pearl was used only as back-up test and never as the sole means of identification. In a sense this has a bearing on chemical tests as well as luminescence tests.

Tests by magnets

The nucleus of a cultured pearl is generally over 90 per cent of the whole pearl with only a very thin skin of nacre covering the mother-of-pearl spherical bead, usually 0.5 mm in 3½ years of growth. A much higher quality control is now exerted than previously and skins are thicker; however, in the early research days the nucleus had a layered banded structure. It was hoped that by suspending a pearl freely between the poles of a powerful electromagnet the magnetic force exerted when the current was switched on would tend to orient the layers of the nucleus in line between the poles of the magnets and that when switched off, the release would be seen as a swing or movement. In the case of natural pearls no such movement would take place since the radial and concentric structure would be equally affected in every radiating direction and no difference or attempted orientation would occur. This early method was neither speedy nor satisfactory.

The lucidoscope

The lucidoscope method devised by M. B. Szilard depended basically upon the fact that nacre (mother-of-pearl) is more transparent to light travelling across the parallel-banded layers than to light travelling down the length. Thus a cultured pearl with a mother-of-pearl bead nucleus would be more transparent to light rays in certain directions than others. Szilard also noted that the effect was not so easily seen in air (dry) as it was if the 'pearl' were immersed in a liquid of similar refractive index to that of nacre (mother-of-pearl). The French authors, J. Galibourg and F. Ryziger in 'Les méthodes d'examen et d'étude des perles fines et des perles de culture' (1927), stated a preference for pure benzine as an immersion liquid because it evaporates quickly and leaves no trace on the pearl specimens. (The danger of liquids to pearls is dealt with in a later section).

The lucidoscope consists of a cell with a transparent base in which the pearl is placed on an iris diaphram (similar to a camera shutter) which excludes from the outer perimeter of the pearl the light which is directed onto it by means of a condenser. Viewing is by either binocular loupe or naked eye, although this was never a positive test.

X-rays

In the later part of the 19th century Sir William Crookes (1832–1919) was experimenting on the effects of electrical discharges through rarified gases in sealed glass tubes. Other workers were also working along similar lines. Crookes found that under conditions of reduced pressure the gas darkened, and the walls of the glass tube glowed with a green fluorescence. A 'Crookes' tube' was the original gas discharge tube to illustrate dark space and cathode glow. Crookes found that the rays emitted by the negative electrode were fast-moving electrons. (Electrons are fundamental particles with a negative electrical charge.) Crookes' work included the discovery of the element thallium, researches into radiant matter and the invention of the radiometer. A short while later Röntgen discovered X-rays. Wilhelm Konrad Röntgen (1845–1923) was a German professor of physics at the University of Würzburg (Bavaria), and in 1895 he discovered rays which were capable of penetrating matter. He termed them 'X-rays' because at the time he did not know what they were. In 1901 he was awarded a Nobel prize for his work.

Röntgen discovered that rays from a discharge tube covered with black paper could cause fluorescence on a barium platino-cyanide screen, and would blacken a photographic plate similarly covered. The power to penetrate light-opaque matter and the variable absorption of these rays by matter opened up a new era of investigation. Considerable excitement and interest was displayed in this new ability to photograph the bones inside the body, and as early as April 1896 the first dental X-ray photograph was taken.

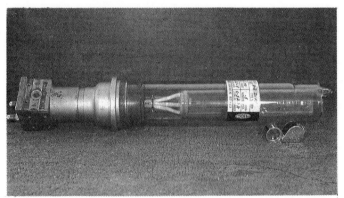

Figure 7.1 X-ray tube used in pearl testing. Note size of the 10× lens in foreground
(Photo: K V Scarratt)

The equipment required to produce X-rays was specialized and not easily obtained. This factor was indeed important and fortunate when the hazardous nature of X-rays and the potential for biological damage was realized. The effect on living cells by intense beams of X-rays is measurable and may be lethal. Nowadays radiographers and others working with such apparatus wear strategically-placed badges. These badges are called 'dosemeters' which are monitored éach four weeks to check any possible radiation effect.

Wavelengths were originally measured in ångström units (Å) which took their name from the Swedish scientist Ander Jon Ångström (1814–1874). The unit is equal to one tenth of a nanometre, i.e. 1 nanometre = 10 ångströms.

X-rays vary in their wavelength from 0.0005 – 100 nanometres. X-rays of wavelengths shorter than one nanometre can penetrate matter deeply. The following table illustrates comparative wavelengths in the electromagnetic spectrum:

X-rays and gamma rays	$0.005 - 100$ nanometres
Ultra-violet rays	$100 - 390$ nanometres
Visible light rays	$390 - 770$ nanometres
Infra-red rays	$770 - 4 \times 10^5$ nanometres
Radio waves	$1 \times 10^5 - 3 \times 10^{13}$ nanometres

X-rays are invisible, as are infra-red and radio waves, but the differences between the characteristics of X-rays and those of light and radio waves are due to their shorter wavelength. X-rays can, however, be detected by their effects on photographic film as well as by their fluorescent effects on sensitized screens, and certain materials. X-rays, like light and radio waves, travel in straight lines and, by experiment, it was found that they could be scattered but would follow only discrete directions in crystalline materials.

The relative X-ray transparencies of certain materials, such as bone, flesh, metal, calcium carbonate and others, is the basis of radiography. The absorption power of the material photographed and the wavelength of the X-rays used shows on a negative film (radiograph or shadowgraph) as contrasts in intensity of exposed portions of the film, i.e. deep-shadowed bone structure, lightly-shaded flesh or tissue areas. The X-ray beams in radiography are absorbed much more by denser materials such as bone, and are less absorbed by flesh, thus, the emerging X-rays have a correspondingly lesser or greater exposure effect upon the film according to the density of the obstruction. The contrast is shown when the film is developed.

In pearl testing fine-grained shadow radiographs are becoming very much more relied upon than ever before to reveal growth structures, or nuclei. Advanced biological techniques used in both mussel and oyster cultured-pearl production, such as the non-nucleus or tissue graft methods, require the laboratory gemmologist to seek as much information as possible from his radiographs. He needs experience of pearls of *known* natural origin (preferably old stock) plus good examples of radiographs of *known* natural and non-nucleus cultured pearls.

The other type of X- photograph is termed a 'lauegram', or 'X-ray diffraction pattern photograph'. Lauegrams are based upon the work and discoveries of Max von Laue, a German physicist, who showed in 1912 that X-rays could be diffracted by a single crystal. Their wavelengths were later found by others to lie in the region of about 0.1 nm. A lauegram is seen to be a collection of small dark spots on the recording film (*Figure 7.2*). When a prominent axis of a thin single crystal is accurately aligned with respect to a narrow pencil of 'white' (continuous wavelength) X-rays passing through crystal, a symmetrical pattern of spots is seen. When it is not aligned, no symmetry in the pattern is discernible. The crystal behaves exactly like a two-dimensional optical crossed grating, the only difference being one of wavelength scale.

By contrast the radiograph or direct shadowgraph is the result of a broader cone of X-rays bathing a larger subject from a greater distance, and no diffraction is involved. Laue was awarded a Nobel prize in 1914 for his work.

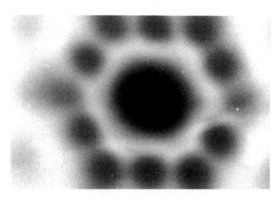

Figure 7.2 A six-spot (hexagonal pattern) X-ray diffraction lauegram of a natural pearl (Photo: A E Farn)

Until about 1913 the method of producing X-rays remained similar in principle to the gas discharge tube discovery of Röntgen. The tube had a different appearance and it was described as an 'ion' or 'cold cathode' tube. This type of tube was later superseded by filament tubes, termed 'Coolidge hot cathode' or 'electron' tubes, in which the electron-beam current can be varied independently. The Coolidge tube was the first to have a heated cathode as a source of electrons.

The electrons are obtained by thermionic emission (thermal energy/high temperature) from a glowing metal filament (the cathode) usually of tungsten (*Figure 7.3*). The beam of electrons emitted by the tungsten filament is accelerated towards the target (anode) by application of a voltage difference between it and the cathode. The target is usually of tungsten for radiography and laue diffraction photography, but the target of the British Gem Testing Laboratory's tube is of molybdenum, whilst the filament is of tungsten.

The method usually employed to produce X-rays is to bombard a metal target with a concentrated beam of electrons. On striking the target the electrons rapidly decelerate and interact with the target to produce X-rays, and it is these which emerge through the 'windows' of the tube while the electrons are absorbed by the windows. There are two windows opposite each other, allowing two lauegrams to be taken simultaneously. The windows, 0.5 mm thick, are of beryllium, a material which absorbs very little of these X-rays actually producing the pattern. Water-cooling is essential due to the large amount of heat generated at the target.

Mention has been made of the fluorescent and sometimes phosphorescent effect X-rays have upon certain materials. When X-rays traverse a material some are absorbed; this energy causes increased atomic vibration, i.e. heating of the material. Some X-rays ionize atoms and produce photoelectrons, i.e. electrons released from a surface by a photon, with or without kinetic energy. (A photon is a quantum of light or of electro-magnetic radiation.) This ionization may result in a secondary ionization, an increase in electrical conductivity and an *emission of visible light*. This visible light is the fluorescent effect seen when freshwater pearls, cultured pearls from sea-water oysters with freshwater shell bead nuclei, or non-nucleus cultured pearls from mussels are irradiated by X-rays.

An extension of this fluorescent effect is that of afterglow, or phosphorescence. When the current is switched off, fluorescence ceases but a continued excited state gives the effect of phosphorescence. This may be minimal and is seen as either an

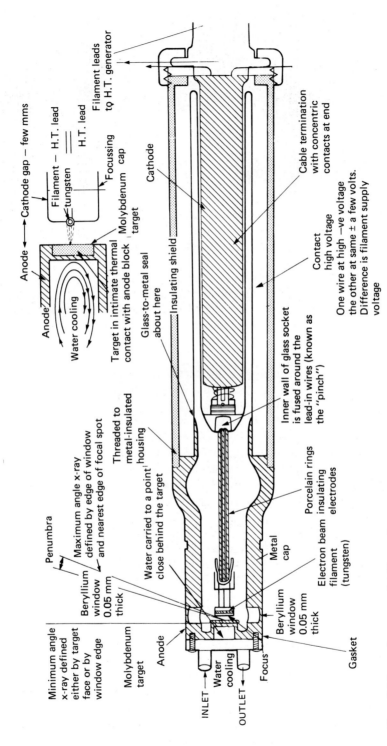

Figure 7.3 Internal structure of an X-ray tube

Figure 7.4 X-ray set opened showing the left-hand cassette in position. A pearl is mounted ready to be turned for the right-hand cassette (Photo: A Jobbins)

Figure 7.5 X-ray set for lauegram with the film cassette on left, pearl on the right to show position. The right-hand cassette is ready to be swung around into position (Photo: A Jobbins)

almost simultaneous dying of the glow, or a visually-prolonged effect. This prolonged characteristic has valuable diagnostic features for the pearl tester/X-ray worker in assessing the provenance of pearls. Non-nucleus cultured pearls from Lake Biwa, Japan, have a distinct tone of colour to their fluorescence and, compared with cultured sea-water pearls, a longer phosphorescence. Overlong exposure to irradiation by X-rays when viewing fluorescence and/or phosphorescence can cause darkening of the nearest surface in some mussel non-nucleated

Figure 7.6 Viewing chamber of X-ray set (Photo: A Jobbins)

Figure 7.7 General scene in pearl-testing laboratory; centre, X-ray powder diffraction camera; left, checking X-ray fluorescence; right, freezing diamonds to enhance their spectra (Photo: A Jobbins)

pearls. The reason for this excited state of fluorescence and phosphorescence is said to be due to traces of manganese in the chemical composition of freshwater pearls and shells. Work and research on this matter was carried out by Dr A. E. Alexander at the Mellon Institute of Industrial Research, Pittsburg.

When a lauegram of a pearl is taken on the purpose-built X-ray set, the pearl is in close contact with the X-ray beam pinhole aperture of 0.7 mm. The film cassette with its intensifying screens is about 7 cm from the pearl.

When a radiograph is to be taken of a pearl necklace, the necklace is usually coiled flat and placed upon a light-tight, black envelope holding a fine-grain film. No pinhole aperture is used and the beryllium window of the tube sheds a broad cone of X-rays downwards to bathe the entire necklace from a distance of 12 to 14 in with an exposure time of 1 to 5 minutes, depending upon the size of the pearls and nature of the film.

A lauegram is obtained when a beam of 'white' X-rays passes through a single crystal which acts like a grating. The emerging diffracted X-rays will follow only discrete directions.

When a beam of X-rays passes through a spherical pearl it is in fact traversing the thin over-lapping sheets or layers of large numbers of single tiny aragonite crystals which comprise the structure of pearl. These microscopically-fine concentric layers

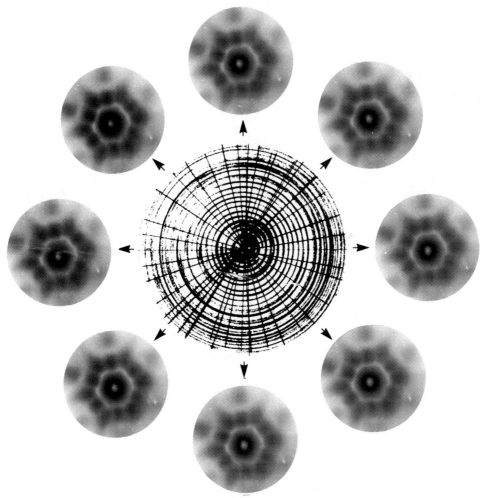

Figure 7.8 Schematic diagram of concentric and radial structure of natural pearl. A six-spot hexagonal pattern is always attained from every direction through the centre of the pearl (Photo: A E Farn)

consist of crystals of orthorhombic aragonite, whose principal crystallographic axes point radially from the centre of the pearl. Crystals of rhombic shape in close-packed conditions assume a pseudo-hexagonal pattern, rather like a honeycomb layer. Thus when the beam of X-rays passes through the pearl centre it follows the main structure pattern and emerges to form a pseudo-hexagonal six-spot trace pattern on the negative film.

Because of the concentric and radial structure of natural pearl, it follows that a second lauegram taken at a right-angle to the first will give a similar pattern. In the case of cultured pearls, i.e. those with a spherical bead nucleus of freshwater shell and an exterior thin skin of natural pearl, the lauegram pattern varies (*Figures 7.8, 7.9, 7.10*).

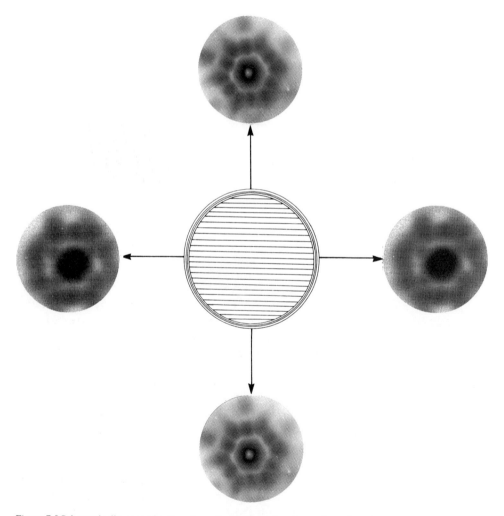

Figure 7.9 Schematic diagram of cultured pearl with banded mother-of-pearl nucleus. A six-spot pattern is obtained perpendicular to the layers. A four-spot pattern is seen parallel to the layers. (Photo: A E Farn)

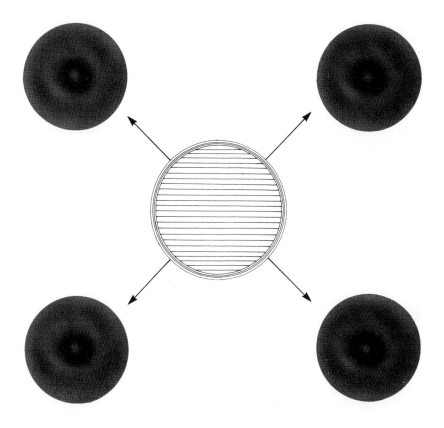

Figure 7.10 Schematic diagram of cultured pearl with mother-of-pearl nucleus. A mixed effect of 4/6 spots merge to a halo effect in positions diagonal to the layer (Photo: A E Farn)

The mother-of-pearl bead inserted into the oyster has a banded layered structure parallel to the shape of the original shell, i.e. it is *not* concentric. In *one direction only* does it give a pseudo-hexagonal pattern and that is the direction at a right angle to the shell layer. In the opposite direction of lower symmetry to the structure it gives a four-spot pattern effect. Thus, when a first lauegram of a pearl is taken and a six-spot pattern results, it is essential to turn the pearl through 90° and take a second lauegram. If this also results in a six-spot pattern then the pearl is natural. However, if the second shows a four-spot pattern the pearl is cultured. Equally, if the first pattern is four-spot then the pearl is cultured and there is no need for a second lauegram.

For lauegram work the pearl is centred on the X-ray beam diaphragm by screw thread adjustment in a purpose-built vice with rubber-clad jaws. Thus the pearl, whether bouton, drop or baroque in shape, can be aligned for its first lauegram exposure. A thin line lightly drawn on the surface of the pearl with a lead pencil facilitates the accurate turning of the pearl, if necessary, through 90° for a second lauegram, thus avoiding guesswork.

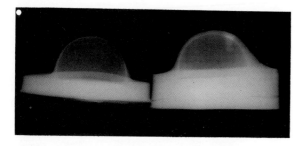

Figure 7.11 Radiograph of Mabe cultured pearls as cut from the oyster shell with rims (Photo: A E Farn)

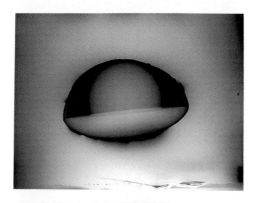

Figure 7.12 Radiograph elevation of a Mabe cultured pearl showing the nucleus and mother-of-pearl base cover (Photo: A E Farn)

Figure 7.13 Cross-section showing the thick outer skin and banded layers in cultured pearls (Photo: B W Anderson)

The X-ray set depicted in *Figure 7.4* is a unique one-off model developed from practical requirements experienced by workers in the British Gem Testing Laboratory and using skills of an interested radiological engineer who developed and designed the set for laboratory pearl-testing requirements. The Laboratory X-ray-generating apparatus has a purpose-built viewing chamber with heavy lead glass windows through which it is possible to observe fluorescence and phosphorescence. This viewing position has been most carefully checked for radiation leakage by specialists from local authorities. It is safer to look through the viewing chamber than to watch television!

The set has a considerable potential for checking fluorescence and phosphorescence in gemstones, synthetics and imitations. Today, with the increase in diamond simulants, it provides a fast, positive method to prove diamond (which is transparent to X-rays) against other simulants which vary in degrees of transparency or opacity. The negative photograph obtained indicates the nature and size of materials tested, which is a security requirement with valuables.

In a small laboratory such as that of the British Gem Testing Laboratory the pearl testers process their own film and thus have a degree of control over the development. This allows for scope in experimentation which is missed in larger organizations where photographic work is carried out by photographers who are not necessarily pearl workers.

Apart from the skill or ability to set up loose pearls or pearl necklaces for X-ray photographic purposes, the real skill lies in the interpretation of the X-ray negative. With radiographs of pearl necklaces, the method is to study details by using a 10× lens of the type seen in the photograph next to and in front of the X-ray tube in *Figure 7.1*.

It is most convenient and comfortable when viewing X-ray negatives, which are usually small, to sit at a bench or desk with an adjustable Anglepoise-type of bench lamp with a 60-watt pearl or opal bulb. The lamp is tilted so that the rim of its shade prevents the light from shining directly into the viewer's eyes.

The negative is studied by holding the film close to the lamp and the viewing lens is held at about 1 to 2 in focus from the film. Care must be taken, if prolonged examination of many pearls is necessary, to avoid heat spoiling the negative which often happens with over-prolonged scrutiny.

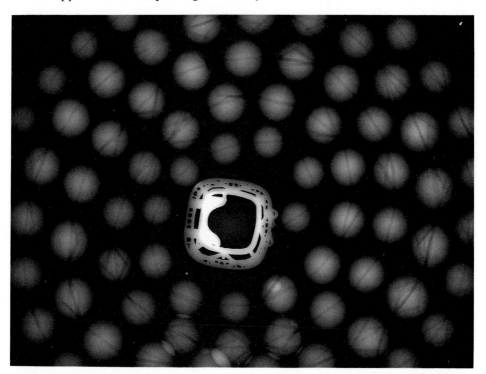

Figure 7.14 Diverted drill holes, due to banded structure of mother-of-pearl nucleus in a cultured pearl necklace (Photo: A E Farn)

Usually it is the straightforward cultured pearls with bead nuclei which are the easiest to determine. The conchiolin ring at the demarcation of bead and thin skin serves as an admirable signal. Much more difficult are fine-quality natural pearls with which radiographs are not so satisfactory.

Fine pearls are the result of steady uninterrupted growth; thus there are no period rings of conchiolin at stages to assist the pearl radiographer. Although with years of practice and constant handling such negatives are reassuring to the expert who knows his pearls, it is not laboratory practice to accept such negatives as positive!

With plenty of pearl-handling in a practical manner the negative can be used as a back-up test to the more intimate views gained by physical examination down the drill holes of such pearls by the 10× lens. Optical examination of interiors is described in the section on the endoscope. Although it may be a cliché to state that practice makes perfect, such is the case with pearl-testing by X-ray methods. The examples shown photographically are the easy and the obvious. In actual working conditions much devolves from sheer experience and practice with thousands of pearls over a lengthy period.

Essentially a radiograph is a photographic study of light and dark shadowy structures, and emphasis should be placed upon the use of the word 'shadowgraph' rather than 'radiograph'.

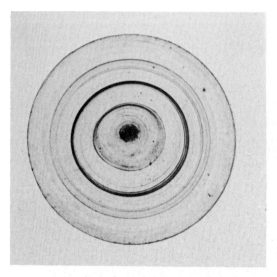

Figure 7.15 Growth period rings in natural pearl (Photo: B W Anderson)

In some radiographs of natural pearls an almost perfect ring structure can be seen, looking very similar to the perfect spheres outlined by conchiolin seen in typical examples of cultured pearls. This deceptive structure is a growth period marked by conchiolin, where perhaps the oyster produces no nacreous secretions and has paused in its normal cycle.

For radiography a fine-grain film is essential to reproduce the fine details seen in some natural pearls of the conchiolin ring near the exterior in cultured pearls. With a steeply-graduated natural-pearl necklace a radiograph is not necessarily the best

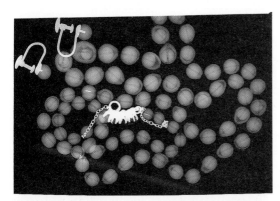

Figure 7.16 Radiograph showing dog-leg drill holes, conchiolin gaps, blisters, bumps, diamond clasp and safety chain in a cultured pearl necklace (Photo: B W Anderson)

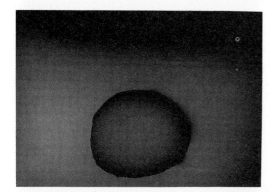

Figure 7.17 Very thick-skinned Australian cultured pearl, with a nucleus deep in centre; the ragged outline is from scissors cuts in the lead shield (Photo: A E Farn)

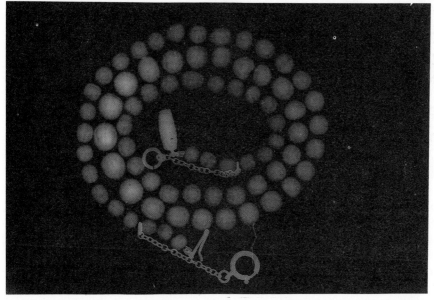

Figure 7.18 Radiograph of a conchiolin-rich natural pearl necklace with possibly three cultured pearls (Photo: A E Farn)

method of testing, since the smallest pearls will be over-exposed and the largest under-exposed. This is because the X-ray beam can penetrate fully the small amount of material in a small end-pearl but cannot achieve the same penetration in the larger central pearls. This motivates the test of every pearl in a presumed natural pearl necklace.

When a large, important pearl is radiographed, it is usually because it is suspected of being a very thick-skinned cultured pearl from Australian waters or the South Seas. These superb-looking 'pearls' often have a bead nucleus which can be as little as one-third of the mass, the remainder being natural pearl. Thus, a considerable amount of natural pearl is encountered by the X-ray beam if the 'pearl' is *lauegrammed* and a confused spot-pattern will arise. Considerable time is taken if a large suspect 'pearl' is radiographed. It has been found that by using the small lead sheet from dental X-ray film as a shield, scattered X-rays which cause fogging can be eliminated. The method is to use a pair of fine pearl stringer's scissors to cut the shape of the pearl out of the lead sheet (like a template or pattern). Several thicknesses can be used according to pearl size and exposure time. When the pearl is placed in its shaped 'hole' considerable improvement of definition is obtained. An example of a thick-skinned Australian cultured pearl is seen in the photograph in *Figure 7.17*. The slightly ragged outline is due to the scissors cutting the lead sheet circle-wise. Almost all of the sphere of the bead nucleus is seen in the exact centre. Exposure times of up to 30 minutes have been necessary on some suspect pearls which may weigh close to 100 grains = 25 carats = 5 gm.

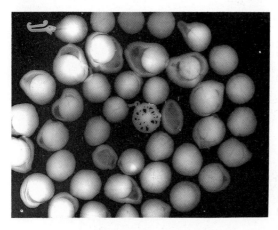

Figure 7.19 Radiograph of baroque cultured pearls with possibly two natural marine non-nucleated cultured pearls
(Photo: A E Farn)

Mention has been made of the increased use and importance of the radiograph compared to the lauegram. The British Gem Testing Laboratory, which started out as a pearl-testing station in 1925, concentrated at first on the endoscope optical method for testing drilled necklace pearls and lauegrams for undrilled or part-drilled pearls.

Because of the rigid trade standards and requirements agreed among themselves by the pearl merchants of the day, every pearl in a necklace had to be separately tested. This involved cutting the silk upon which they were strung and separately

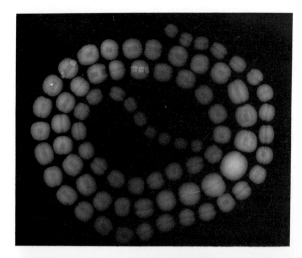

Figure 7.20 Radiograph of poor-quality natural pearls showing drill holes plugged with seed pearls, imitation and broken broachers (Photo: A E Farn)

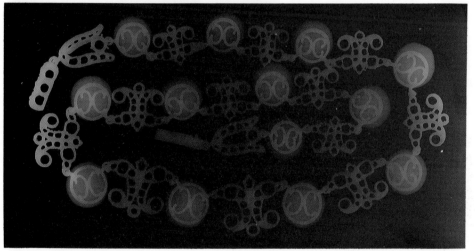

Figure 7.21 Radiograph of non-nucleated flat button cultured pearls mounted on a diamond necklace. Diamonds are transparent to X-rays and appear as holes (Photo: A E Farn)

examining each pearl by the endoscope method. A radiograph would not prove every single natural pearl in a photograph of a pearl necklace since natural growth structures in fine pearls are not easily seen. On the other hand, a cultured-pearl necklace is an ideal subject for a radiograph. This is due to the regularity of the conchiolin fine-line definition around the spherical mother-of-pearl bead insert which is close to the perimeter of the cultured pearl.

At least two major X-ray generating sets have been purpose-built for the laboratory's use and over the years considerable expertise and experienced technique has evolved in the lauegram method of testing undrilled pearls. However, the arrival of non-nucleated cultured pearls from freshwater mussels made the acceptance of two lauegrams each of six-spot pattern less positive as a proof of natural pearl, even though the type of lauegram pattern was somewhat indicative of a non-nucleus cultured pearl. The mere fact that some non-nucleus cultured six-spot patterns looked like the 'halo' type pattern obtained from some Australian natural pearls in a certain direction was sufficient to undermine the absolute authority of the lauegram which had prevailed up to the advent of non-nucleated cultured pearls.

Resort had to be made to shadowgraphs. Fortunately, in the case of the necklaces of non-nucleus cultured pearls these were very satisfactory. Although no spherical bead nucleus is seen, the body substance of the non-nucleus cultured

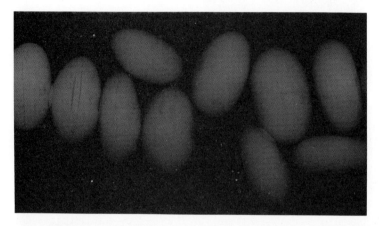

Figure 7.22 Some of the 'pearls' removed from the necklace shown in *Figure 7.21* and radiographed (Photo: A E Farn)

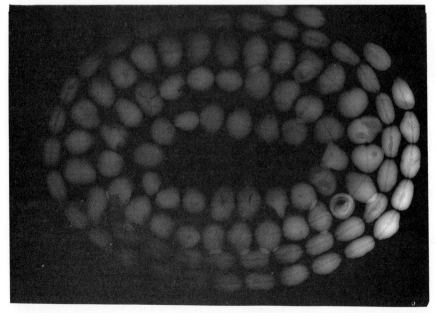

Figure 7.23 Radiographs of sizes and shapes of non-nucleated pearls in a necklace (Photo: A E Farn)

pearls does show faint structure lines with characteristic central shapes and outlines which are never seen in shadowgraphs of natural mussel pearls.

In natural pearl no two pearls are alike in their radiographic portrayal; usually the evidence, if any, is tenuous. With non-nucleus cultured pearls evidence is visible in practically every pearl as embryo-like vermiform structures. Not only is this regularity of structure seen but the added characteristic of distinctive fluorescence and long phosphorescence adds powerful evidence to the final decision.

However, the saga of natural *v* cultured pearl is an ongoing performance. The 1920s–1930s period saw considerable advance in optical and X-ray methods against the nucleated mother-of-pearl bead cultured pearl. Specific gravity values were established, chemical core scrapings and their fluorescence/phosphorescence seemed to have decided the issue. 'Progress', if this is the word, has now been made in furthering the process of nucleation of some freshwater Biwa mussels with large beads; but worse, the introduction of the non-nucleus method into salt-water oysters in Australian and other warm waters demands further researches. These products are now giving radiographer/pearl-testers considerable problems (*Figure 7.24*). The useful adjunct of fluorescence and/or phosphorescence is missing since sea-water oysters do not produce nacre with the required traces of manganese (the fluorescing constituent of freshwater pearl shell).

Using the larger pearl oyster, *Pinctada margaritifera,* and probably *Pinctada maxima,* the larger 'pearl' produced usually has sufficient 'pearl' surrounding the non-nucleus to make a clear interpretation of the images difficult or even

Figure 7.24 Radiograph of three Australian cultured pearls, four non-nucleated cultured pearls and one natural pearl (Photo: A E Farn)

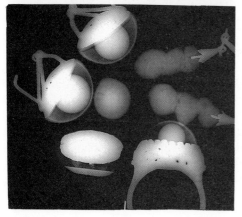

Figure 7.25 Radiograph showing Mabe ear clips, non-nucleated ear pendants, natural pearl, de Meisner imitation and Mabe cultured pearl ring (Photo: A E Farn)

impossible. The non-nucleus shape can look very much like the centres seen of 'mud' in some large pearls. All told, the biological knowledge gained from the revelations of many workers in the early days of discussion on the 'origin of pearls' has benefited the cultured-pearl producers. Much has been written and concentration appears to have centred on cultured pearls and their production on a large commercial scale. If any comfort can be derived from these somewhat worrying factors, it is that their sheer volume affords scope for familiarization with their characteristics, rather as we do with popular prints of famous artists originals.

The remarkable growth in cultured-pearl production, said to be increasing by 10 per cent per year, is due to the fundamental factor that cultured pearls offer the highest return of profit of all marine products cultivated in coastal waters.

Figure 7.26 A pearl as a nucleus in a cultured pearl. A drill hole extends through both (Photo: R K Mitchell)

Figure 7.27 Two pieces of natural pearl joined and the join hidden by clever mounting (Photo: A E Farn)

Despite initial set-backs in identification caused by clever cultivation methods, positive methods will follow by virtue of necessity and the demand for natural pearls.

The advent of the first spherical cultured pearls in the legitimate pearl markets of the world appeared to cause a drop in sales of natural pearls, and at first sight this would appear to be expected. However, in a personal note from B. W. Anderson, the first official pearl (laboratory) tester in Great Britain – and probably in the world – he states: 'It was lack of supply of pearls from the Persian Gulf rather than a fall in demand by the pearl-buying public on account of the rise of the cultured pearl.' He continues by quoting figures for the yearly tests on pearls, and opines that the Wall Street crash, the consequent world slump and the onset of the Second World War distorted trade figures. Pearl-testing figures for the 1950s and 1960s were maintained at a level higher than that achieved in 1928, which was the peak of the pearl boom in London and Paris. This indicates that natural pearls were in demand in pre-war years and are much more so today despite the huge commercial activity in the cultured pearl arena.

A significant factor highlighting the rarity value of natural pearls is that cultured pearl production is quoted in TONS!

Testing by endoscope

The endoscope method of testing drilled necklace pearls was an achievement of the French workers C. Chilowski and A. Perrin (1926). Their apparatus was modified

Figure 7.28 Mother-of-pearl nameplate to an endoscope (Photo: R K Mitchell)

by two other French workers, Simon and Réné Bloch, whose names appear appropriately on a semi-circular-shaped piece of mother-of-pearl on each instrument (*Figure 7.28*).

The method

The method is essentially the use of the ability of the structures of natural pearl (radial and concentric) and of cultured pearls (mainly banded or layered) to allow light to travel either around the concentric layers or straight out via the straight-banded layers.

The light source for the endoscope was originally a carbon arc (the first 25 instruments imported into London were of this variety), but doubtless flexible light sources and high-intensity lamps would now supply the lighting. The endoscope is best used in conditions of semi-darkness, with no lighting behind the seated operator. In the early days, due to the direct current employed, a rubber mat was placed under the feet because of the somewhat hazardous nature of the electrical wiring. The operator is shielded from the intense light of the carbon arcs by a black housing which also supports one end of the optical system of condensing lenses, used to feed the intense beam of light through a hollow platinum needle.

The needle has two highly-polished metal mirrors inserted in the tube end; these are inclined at 45° to each other in opposing senses. What might be termed as the point or end of the needle is one of the mirrors at 45°; this is nearer to the operator. The second mirror, at an opposite angle of 45°, faces the source of light. The needles vary slightly in their exterior diameter from 0.3 mm to 0.5 mm.

The operator, seated in an 'elbows-up' position, views the end mirror through a low-powered, horizontally-mounted microscope. The hollow needle has a small aperture cut into the tube next to the mirror nearer to the light source. Above the

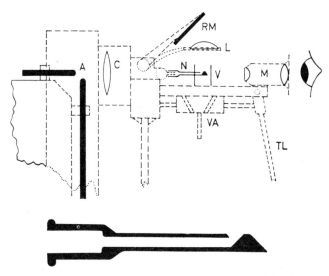

Figure 7.29 Schematic diagram of the endoscope: A, arc-light; C, condenser; RM, reflecting mirror to show surface of pearl; L, lens to enlarge surface of pearl; N, needle; V, vice to hold pearl; M, microscope to view end of needle; VA, vice adjustment; TL, traversing lever to move pearl along needle. *Lower diagram:* Enlarged section of needle (Reproduced by permission from R. Webster's *Gems,* 4th edn (Butterworth), revised by B. W. Anderson)

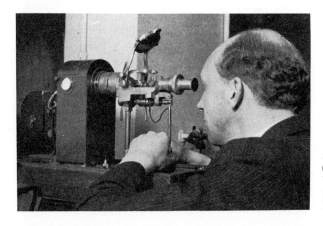

Figure 7.30 The endoscope in use (Reproduced by permission from R. Webster's *Gems,* 4th edn (Butterworth), revised by B. W. Anderson)

needle and mounted in a brass stirrup is a bi-convex lens which allows the enlarged view of the surface of the pearl on the needle to be viewed in a mirror mounted similarly above the lens at 45° to the plane of the endoscope tube.

When the light source is switched on and the endoscope needle is mounted on its receiving stub, a bright light shoots through the hollow needle, and escapes via the aperture of the needle next to the first mirror which is at 45° to the line of the needle. If a natural drilled pearl is then carefully threaded or placed upon the needle, the escaping beam of light will enter a concentric layer and travel round that layer by the process of total reflection. The beam of light is now trapped inside the concentric layer and cannot emerge until the pearl is carefully moved along the needle to reach a position where the two mirrors in opposite senses are in the concentric centre of the pearl layers. The beam of totally reflected light will escape via the second inclined mirror and be seen by the operator as a small bright flash. The pearl is moved gently along the needle by a traversing lever, whilst the operator views the end mirror through the low-powered microscope. If a cultured pearl is placed on the needle the light cannot pass round concentric layers but follows the banded layers to emerge at the outside of the cultured pearl, looking like a streak of light, or 'cat's-eye' effect. This is seen when glancing up at the mirror mounted above the optical system at an angle of 45° to allow seated observation.

Effectiveness

The endoscope is considered to be 100 per cent effective and accurate in the hands of the skilled operator. Even in a case of a conchiolin-rich centre in a natural pearl which causes a sharp cut-off of light travelling round concentrically, the effect is recognized in the observation mirror as characteristic of natural pearl. Rotating the conchiolin-rich-centred pearl upon the needle will confirm this cut-off characteristic, whereas a cultured pearl which might have looked similar will, upon being rotated, give a definite cat's-eye effect typical of cultured pearls.

The endoscope is still used in France, and was only dropped from use in England some time after the Second World War, owing to difficulties of obtaining parts and, at the time, the manufacture of small consignments of hollow platinum needles. At that time the physical handling of somewhere in the region of 2½ million drilled pearls and the examination of their interiors via their drill holes had given the Laboratory enormous experience and knowledge of natural pearls. Eventually, optical examination, backed by radiography where required, together with fluorescence and phosphorescence effects, saw the demise of the endoscope in the London Laboratory.

It is sad when such skills or apparatus disappear, even though rapid and accurate examinations of pearl necklaces are carried out by other means. The endoscope afforded opportunity to study the direction of mother-of-pearl banding in cultured pearls, and the measurement of the thickness of the outside skin of cultured pearls by means of calibrated scales attached to the traversing lever. B. W. Anderson and C. J. Payne could average 200 pearls an hour using the endoscope method.

Production figures

Pearl testing, to combat the new intrusion of cultured pearls, began in London in 1925. The early figures available show the year's figures for 1926 doubled by 1927 and increased tenfold by 1928. The slump period figures centred on the early 1930s and then began to improve in 1936, 1937 and 1938, but the Second World War caused another set-back until 1946, from when figures were fairly evenly spread to 1970 with one enormous year of 1955. It is difficult to attribute to the figures of each year between natural and cultured because some figures will be entirely for cultured pearl necklaces, probably sent by a jeweller for his valuation service. Other years saw second-hand pearl necklaces being sold for death duty payments, and again when Purchase Tax was high it could be avoided on second-hand goods. Thus, the figures in *Tables 7.1* and *7.2* are not necessarily a record of cultured pearls detected or masquerading as natural, although examples were found in some Bombay bunches.

Despite the apparent drop in the 1970s, the trend shows a gradual rise again in figures and the author is reliably informed of a continuation in the annual figures for pearl testing. The demand has been from Arab purchasers through the Hatton Garden and London West End sources of supply. The Arabs and the Indians are consistent in their appreciation of fine pearls.

TABLE 7.1. Natural pearls and cultured pearls tested at the London Laboratory

Year	Pearls		Year	Pearls		Year	Pearls	
------	*Natural*	*Cultured*	------	*Natural*	*Cultured*	------	*Natural*	*Cultured*
1926	4 973	421	1946	62 616	7 553	1966	72 714	20 684
1927	10 182	864	1947	62 121	8 629	1967	65 921	23 729
1928	49 068	1 220	1948	62 344	11 082	1968	74 237	28 155
1929	45 306	1 885	1949	58 588	13 020	1969	61 370	21 790
1930	30 396	1 380	1950	60 180	11 211	1970	67 519	20 102
1931	7 134	305	1951	66 545	15 046	1971	43 605	16 776
1932	15 771	371	1952	63 430	13 101	1972	26 322	17 304
1933	24 908	455	1953	50 364	11 990	1973	19 000	11 104
1934	34 662	2 182	1954	62 845	15 432	1974	19 274	15 108
1935	30 124	1 230	1955	138 484	15 191	1975	19 659	15 398
1936	42 288	3 002	1956	73 585	16 284	1976	27 261	11 620
1937	40 444	2 222	1957	56 589	15 596	1977	21 883	9 842
1938	41 052	2 545	1958	51 020	13 995	1978	25 401	15 949
1939	26 848	1 768	1959	52 359	15 560	1979	31 364	14 028
1940	14 119	1 404	1960	57 243	14 506	1980	41 993	15 897
1941	9 624	2 035	1961	61 185	17 975	1981	35 737	19 155
1942	15 035	2 525	1962	72 194	19 572	1982	119 264	22 958
1943	24 249	4 004	1963	70 105	20 700	1983	62 149	20 154
1944	28 485	3 073	1964	79 393	22 046	1984	72 911	21 042
1945	36 806	3 665	1965	74 282	21 224			

In this Table: *Natural pearls* tested mainly by endoscope   2 464 440
              Cultured pearls tested by X-ray and endoscope   593 751

Specific gravity (SG) tests

The London Chamber of Commerce Laboratory, which started in 1925 as a pearl-testing station, carried out extensive SG determinations on pearls from various sources and cultured pearls from Japan. Facilities and time existed for such research and the figures for SGs are reliable and very soundly based. Equally, in the section on SGs in their 1927 paper 'Les méthodes d'examen et d'étude des perles fines et des perles de cultures' (*Revue d'Optique Théorique et Instrumentale*,

1927) the French workers J. Galibourg and F. Ryziger give broadly similar figures. Anderson, on page 395 of his book *Gem Testing* (9th edn 1980) and on page 505 of his 1983 revision of Webster's *Gems: Their Sources, Descriptions and Identification*, gives useful details of pearl SGs. Looking at the chart, it is seen that Persian Gulf and Gulf of Mannar pearls vary from 2.67 to 2.78, and overall pearl SGs range from 2.61 to 2.78. Cultured pearls from Japan have an SG of 2.72 to 2.78 and the range for the non-nucleated freshwater variety is 2.67 to 2.70.

The mother-of-pearl bead nucleus used in Japanese cultured pearls came from Mississippi freshwater mussel shell. This had an SG of 2.82, but since most Japanese cultured pearls have only a relatively thin skin of natural pearl, their average SG ranges between 2.72 and 2.78.

TABLE 7.2. Pearl specific gravities

Source	Bivalve mollusc	Colour	SG Range
Persian Gulf	P. radiata	Creamy white	2.68–2.74
Gulf of Mannar	P. radiata	Pales cream white	2.68–2.74
N coast Australia	P. margaritifera	Silvery white	2.68–2.78
NW coast Australia	P. maxima	Silvery white	2.67–2.78
Shark Bay, W Australia	P. carchariarum	Yellow	2.67–2.78
Venezuela	P. radiata	White	2.65–2.75
Japan	P. martensi	White/greenish	2.66–2.76
Freshwater pearls			
N America	Margaritifera	White	2.66 to over 2.78
Europe	Margaritifera	White	2.66 to over 2.78
Florida and Gulf of California	Strombus gigas (great conch)	Pink	2.85
Gulf of California	Haliotidae (the Abalone)	Green Yellow Blue	2.61–2.69
Gulf of California		Black	2.61–2.69
Cultured pearl SGs			
Japan	P. martensi } P. radiata	White	2.72–2.78
Japan, Lake Biwa non-nucleated	Hyriopsis schlegeli	White	2.67–2.70

Non-nucleated cultured pearls from Australian *Pinctada maxima* and *Pinctada margaritifera* will not be usefully indicated by SG tests.

Very accurate SG determinations were a particular strength of the (then) London Chamber of Commerce Laboratory, whether of fine small items of less than one carat size to large carvings. Facilities for hydrostatic weighings are not always easily available or to hand for individuals, and thus a more generalized method is utilized based on differences between average SGs of natural and cultured pearls. The method is of floatation in a liquid of *known* SG. Such a liquid is made by adding monobromonaphthalene to bromoform, in which a piece of Iceland spar remains in suspension. Iceland spar (pure calcite) has an SG of 2.710.

Monobromonaphthalene, which has a somewhat off-putting smell of mothballs (naptha), does not evaporate as could other dilutants such as benzene or toluene.

Ideally, the liquid should be stored in a ground-glass-stoppered cylindrical glass container in which the liquid can be shaken, and observed, and the calcite rhomb seen in suspension. The majority 80 per cent of oriental pearls in this solution will float and slightly denser ones will sink slowly; the majority of cultured pearls will sink decisively. Obviously the pearls should not be left in this solution; the author has noted how speedily such liquids can be washed from tested items by jets of cold water.

   An indication of the need to rinse quickly may be drawn from the following incident. After somewhat unsatisfactory radiographs had been taken of a part-drilled pearl, a lauegram was not available. The pearl was then checked in a density liquid. A second radiograph taken as routine revealed enhanced ring structures/growth periods which had not been visible previously due to absorption of the heavy element bromine in the bromoform liquid. As a heavy element it absorbed some of the X-rays whereas the pearl substance offered less obstruction to the rays. When the film was developed, the effect was seen in the enhanced fine line structure of what proved to be a natural pearl.

The chemical composition of pearls

The deposition of calcium in biological systems is called 'calcification'. Broadly speaking, pearls are composed of calcium carbonate, conchiolin and water. The calcium carbonate is represented in the structure usually as aragonite in overlapping concentrically-placed sheets of crystals. The conchiolin is the amorphous scleroprotein material which acts as the mortar in the lattice framework. The percentages vary according to several authorities, which is reasonable when one considers that we have a crystalline material arranged in an

TABLE 7.3. Chemicals in parts per million in the composition of pearls

Element compound	Salt-water oysters			Freshwater mussels
	Pinctada martensi	Pinctada margaritifera	Pinctada maxima	Hyriopsis schlegeli
H_2O	0.51	0.48	0.51	0.38
Ig loss	45.86	46.16	46.04	45.66
CaO(%)	53.28	53.14	52.87	53.29
Mg	140	190	349	40
Sr	1157	1220	1616	312
K	54	48	56	48
Li	1	1	0	0
Cu	1.3	0	5	0.6
Zn	2.5	1.9	3.5	4.6
Mn	16	16	20	476
Cl	993	1041	815	208
SO_4	1515	1836	1826	561
P	60	9	4	150

organic setting, together with a reasonable amount of water (*see* Chapter 1 for figures).

In the testing of pearls, particularly the rapid and useful separation of freshwater products from salt-water material, use is made of the fluorescence and phosphorescence characteristics manifested under X-ray excitation, effects for which the trace element manganese is responsible . Considerable work was carried out by Dr A. E. Alexander on this subject. In *Table 7.3* supplied Dr K. Wada, Research Officer, National Pearl Research Laboratory, Kashikojima, Mie Prefectore, Japan, the amounts of manganese in parts per million are given for salt-water (oyster) pearls and freshwater (mussel) pearls. These are 16 for *Pinctada margaritifera* and 476 for *Hyriopsis schlegeli.* In the accompanying chart the quantities in parts per million are given for a range of other trace elements. *Pinctada martensi* is the original pearl oyster from Japan, now used in pearl culture.

Chapter 8
Imitation pearls

To imitate or to copy something implies that the object imitated possesses qualities which are desirable and is therefore worthy of copying. Imitation is said to be the best form of flattery. Man throughout the ages has copied or imitated precious gems – usually because the rarity and value of the natural products place them beyond the grasp of ordinary men.

Figure 8.1 Radiograph of a necklace of glass imitation pearls (opaque to X-rays) (Photo: R Webster)

As has been quoted earlier, in their opening lines *The Book of the Pearl*, Kunz and Stevenson begin their description of pearls as follows: 'Perfected by nature and requiring no art to enhance their beauty, pearls were naturally the earliest gems known to prehistoric man'. The imitation of pearls by man is a token of esteem in which natural pearls continued to be held. The early imitations were 'pearl' coloured. The imitation of coloured natural pearls came later as man began to increase his appreciation and knowledge of the varieties of and colours of pearls.

In the early days following the discovery of America and of Cortez's conquistadors, the existence of fantastic hoards of pearls was recorded. The rough seamen and soldiers alike would seize these collections and label them as 'pearls'. It is now known that although many were indeed pearls, there were frequently among them beads of spheres of mother-of-pearl cut from the thickest part of the shell. These must rank as examples of the very earliest imitations. It is understandable that the natives who cut and polished them did so because of the attractive nacreous nature of the shell and it was, of course, the carapace home of the natural pearl.

Most of the hoards of pearls found in Indian burial mounds of cremated remains were ruined by fire and among these some imitation pearls were also found. These were spherical pellets of clay which had coverings of pulverized heat-treated micaceous powder applied to them. Doubtless the resilient nature of the mica was lessened by the heat, but the subtle myriad reflections would contribute a 'schiller' to these early imitation pearls.

Venetian glass

The Spaniard's habit of forcing natives to dive continuously for pearls off the Venezuelan coast, and their impatience at the rapidly-diminishing catch despite all kinds of improvisation to garner the harvest from the sea-beds, resulted in an almost total drying-up of the supply of pearls. So much had the sea-bed been raked and swept that pearl merchants turned to manufacturing imitation pearls, and these had to compete with others already appearing upon the scene. From Venice, where mastery of the art of glass manufacture had been achieved, there were glass beads which were hollow and iridescent and had a filling of wax to give them the appearance of solidity.

'Roman pearls'

The most attractive and beautiful imitation pearls were hollow glass beads which had their interiors painted with *essence d'orient* and filled with wax. These were given the name 'Roman pearls' and were the achievement of a French rosary-maker named Jaquin who, at the end of the 17th century, produced them in his kitchen at Passy, just outside Paris. He had noticed that water in which bleak (a small fish from the Seine) had been scaled, had a nacreous reflection. Closer observation showed that the reflective effect was produced by the disintegration of dissolving of the fine thin film which covered the scales of the fish. He filtered the water and recovered the nacreous/reflective material, mixed it with a form of varnish, and called it *'essence d'orient'*. *Orient* in this case is possibly the 'orient' of pearl, i.e. its play of colour reflective effect; *essence* being in French variously 'essential', 'oil' or 'extract'. The scales of the bleak (*Alburnus lucidus*) were the principal source of the *essence d'orient* manufactured in France.

Some authorities attribute the *'orient'* in *essence d'orient* as an acknowledgement that the Chinese knew of this pearly varnish long before Jaquin's discovery.

Depending upon the method of extraction and quality of material, it is estimated that two million bleak are required to provide a litre of essence. Further investigation of the substance found that the iridescence was caused by minute crystals embedded in the skin covering the fish scales. By careful analysis these were found to be an organic material named 'guanine', a waste material secreted by the fish and closely allied to uric acid. Guanine is fairly stable; it withstands heat, is insoluble in certain solvents, is non-toxic and is chemically inert. Other materials, notably salts of lead, used in the manufacture of imitation pearls, are now prohibited as they are dangerous to health.

The demand for bleak scales was high and constant. From the River Thames a million francs' worth of bleak scales were exported to France each year. Later, the Norwegian sardine herring proved a better source of pearl essence. The French set up a factory in Norway, complete with trained chemists, maintaining a continuous quality control on the product. The Second World War halted this work and the process went to America. Various countries are now busy manufacturing *essence d'orient* and, surprisingly, there is a continuing demand for the product. The best source of fish scales now is the Bay of Fundy on the New Brunswick coast of eastern Canada. Herring by the tens of thousands are caught and loaded into crates with open slatted bottoms. As they turn and toss they shed their scales which are collected from beneath the open slats. The scales are rushed to a factory for processing. Because of the extreme bitter cold they arrive in good frozen condition. The final filtration or purification is suspended in a special solvent before being added to a cellulose lacquer. This is the end-product to which a colouring agent is added if 'fancy' imitation pearls are required.

There are other products which depend upon inorganic materials producing plately crystallites which, due to their near-parallel structure, create an iridescent effect through the diffraction of light at the surface plus the interference effect of light reflected from the thin films.

Roman imitation pearls

The mention of 'Roman pearls', i.e. wax-filled beads, must not be confused with the imitation pearls made in Roman times which were glass beads silvered and then coated with another coating of glass. The Roman imitations were due to the enormous demand and cult among the Roman people for real pearl jewellery which could not always be satisfied.

Natural products which are used as imitations of pearls have a certain basis for respect more than does synthetic lacquer coating, etc, to glass artefacts. Dr A. E.

Alexander, the American gemmologist, who did research on pearls and fluorescence at the Mellon Institute, has a point when he states that pearls cannot be synthesized, they can only be imitated.

Imitation cultured pearls

'Imitation cultured pearls' as a description is a little bizarre. To imitate pearls is the ultimate tribute to pearls. To imitate cultured pearls seems a second-rate sort of next best. These so-called imitation cultured pearls pose a certain danger to the skilled radiographer/gemmologist employed in a trade gem-testing laboratory. They are composed of a mother-of-pearl bead and coated with a form of 'essence d'orient' or synthetic pearl essence.

A major portion of the work in a busy laboratory is pearl testing, that is, determining natural or cultured pearls. Contrary to opinions expressed in some works on pearls, the accent of recent years has been upon *natural* pearls. Thus, in a busy laboratory, one has a flow of both natural and cultured pearls to test. These may take the form of necklaces of drilled pearls, part-drilled pearls mounted as earrings, brooches, studs, rings, etc. They can be nucleated cultured pearls, non-nucleated cultured pearls and composite cultured pearls such as Mabes. The accent in modern testing is on speed where the method usually is radiography assisted by X-ray diffraction (lauegrams), and both fluorescent and phosphorescent excitation by X-rays. Herein lies the danger from the mother-of-pearl bead coated with pearl essence. Usually, to a laboratory worker, they do not look natural pearls. Thus a preliminary check for fluorescence gives a positive reaction followed by positive phosphorescence (as for cultured pearl). A lauegram would yield a four-spot as well as a six-spot pattern, both of which obtained in cultured pearls. Unless the gemmologist uses his simple 10× lens for a careful scrutiny he could make a mistake whilst using his sophisticated X-ray apparatus, or as Jean Taburiaux in his *La Perle et Ses Secrets* says: 'It is necessay to rub lightly the pearl against one of your teeth. The imitation pearl glides smoothly whereas the natural and the cultured pearls are rough. This method of our grandmother is infallible and merits a trial experiment.' A little learning can be dangerous whereas a little practical experience is rewarding.

Another tricky form of imitation is that of a pearly protuberance cut from a shell and carefully polished at the edge. When skilfully mounted this proves difficult to determine because it resembles a natural poor-quality baroque pearl, and it would need unsetting to prove positively.

Other solid beads imitating pearls are produced in glass and in plastics materials. The plastics, which are light in weight compared to glass and natural pearl, do not hang well as a necklace. They are seldom knotted and have a remarkably consistent similarity in colour and hue. Although it is not a test, as is the tooth test, an experienced laboratory worker should be able to *feel* the difference between imitation and natural pearls.

Although the Chinese – *circa* 3000 BC – covered flat models of Buddha with a nacreous coating by placing them in fresh-water mussels, these were not imitation pearls. A letter from a French priest in Peking in November 1734 describes a superior form of imitation pearl produced by the Chinese. It is made from pulverized seed-pearl powder moistened with the juice of holly leaves and rolled into spheres the size of peas. When dry they are inserted into mussels which have been carefully selected and stored in freshwater containers. The mussels are kept and fed for 100 days by pellets comprised of a concentration of mixed powdered roots of medical herbs and honey. No details are given of the extraction of the spherical (?) 'pearls' or whether in fact they became attached to the nacreous shell lining. As stated previously, the use of natural materials to imitate other natural materials has some merit.

Imitation Pink Pearls

Among natural pearls, those found in the univalve, *Strombus gigas,* which has a beautiful pink interior, are the Conch Pearls or Pink Pearls. These are quite heavy, having specific gravity (SG) of 2.85, and have a pattern on the surface variously described as 'flame pattern', 'watered silk', or 'silk' as seen in some sapphires. They are non-nacreous. These Pink Pearls are often oval or drop-shaped; they are seldom large and their colour has a tendency to fade towards their extremities. Their density divorces them from pink coral which superficially can look like Pink Pearl; both, of course, are calcium carbonate but the SG of coral lies between 2.6 and 2.7. Coral has a form of banded or zonal surface pattern which again distinguishes it from Pink Pearl. Pink Pearls of symmetrical shape, good colour and reasonable size are today worth quite respectable sums of money. Glass can easily imitate both coral and Pink Pearl. Usually, however, small bubbles near the surface help in identification as does density and sometimes swirl striae. Only once, to the author's knowledge, has a pink bead shown a peculiar pattern which could have been though of as 'flame pattern'. Normally a trade laboratory has few occasions to examine or test Pink Pearls, and so, of course, even fewer examples of imitation of Pink Pearls are seen.

Imitation black pearls

Imitation black pearls are not so common as other colour imitations since the true black pearl has a colour which is far from being a matt black. It has, in fact, a beautiful sheen, sometimes a greenish hue to a black background and at other times a bluish-black colour which is very difficult to describe adequately. Tahiti is the pearl centre of the Pearl Islands from whence come natural black pearls, and naturally-coloured black cultured pearls. Before the advent of attractive cultured black pearls the demand for the extremely rare natural black pearls was confined to a somewhat exclusive clientele who appreciated these pearls of very rare colours, and had sufficient money to purchase them.

It is mostly in late Victorian to Edwardian jewellery that one sees serious attempts to imitate natural black pearls. These imitations were usually of haematite or polished anthracite. The haematite beads had a metallic lustre and, being an iron oxide, were extremely heavy (SG around 5.00). They were soft, and if rubbed against a non-porcellaneous (unglazed) substance (sometimes termed a 'streak plate') they would leave a distinctive red streak, a deposit of powdered haematite. The polished anthracite beads, according to one authority, have a peculiar structure which may have persuaded some to imagine them to be black pearls. Less often seen or mistaken are the extra-terrestrial tektites, sometimes referred to as 'black fellows buttons'. They are glass-like, often black and found mostly in various states in Australia. They have a concretionary exterior appearance and density and hardness ranges which fit broadly into those of glass.

Today's imitation pearls are manufactured on a huge commercial scale as costume jewellery with hardly a danger to the real pearl market. *See also* the section on Black Pearls.

Costume pearls

Thus imitation pearls are found in graduated and choker necklets of such sizes and matching symmetry and colour as to divorce them completely even from cultured pearls by reason of the extremely high price such sizes would command. The give-away signs in most necklace imitation pearls is at the drill hole. This is never so precise as in natural or cultured pearls which are individually drilled. The imitation mass-produced pearls literally have their hall-mark at the drill hole which shows signs of unevenness and the sprue-like formations due to the lack of finish applied to the manufactured bead. Thick 'tears' of the coating may appear at the drill hole as coagulations. An examination with a 10× lens will quickly and easily reveal these tell-tale signs. Equally, an examination of the surface of glass beads will reveal bubbles just below the surface, or a matt pattern totally unlike the wandering serrated cloissons seen in natural pearls.

At one time imitation pearls were manufactured by the action of soft fusible glass from a blowpipe flame dropping onto fine copper wire which, when turned by the operator, produced a spherical blob. Acid was used to dissolve the copper wire, thus leaving behind a ready-made 'drill hole' for the threading. This method has been superseded by a coated-wire system which needs no acid but having a flame-proof coating the wire allows the formations of the fused glass bead and permits the withdrawal of the bead from the wire.

Glass beads for imitation pearl necklases are sometimes strung in widely-spaced graduation on a board – perhaps as many as 50, with 100 rows to a board. The boards with the 'necklaces' strung proud are dipped into *essence d'orient*. The board is turned to assist even coating and so also to prevent running or tears. Several coats of essence are applied, during which time rotation in a dust-free atmosphere helps the drying of each coating whilst ensuring an even layering.

Another method used for a higher-quality imitation pearl is to mount each glass bead separately on a metal (brass) stalk. These stalks can be as many as 100 upwards to 500 on a cork board. The number of beads per board obviously depends upon the sizes of beads being used. Each board, bristling with mounted beads, is dipped into *essence d'orient* for a brief second and then placed in a drier. The action is repeated many times until the colour depth or quality of finish desired is reached. When thoroughly dried, each imitation pearl is removed from its stalk and the sprue (or extrusion) of essence formed by drips at the drill hole is carefully removed.

De Meisner pearls

Imitation pearls which come under the heading of 'made to measure' are de Meisner pearls which were made from a fine matt glass and had a mother-of-pearl base similar to the finish of a Mabe cultured blister pearl (*Figure 7.25*).

These pearls often were hand-made to imitate very expensive natural pearl. When natural pearls, readily recognizable by their size, shape and colour, were pledged or offered as collateral, their owners, not wishing the pearls' absence to be noticed, had skilful replacement copies made.

It may be of interest to readers to note that the author first saw an example in 1976. Its owners, a prominent West End jeweller, described de Meisner imitations as pre-1939–1945 war products. The radiograph of the de Meisner showed an opaque mass and partially-transparent base. It was a baroque 'pearl' set in a brooch with a surround of baguette-cut and brillant-cut diamonds. When unset, the 'pearl' weighed 142 grains whereas if it had been natural pearl it should have been between 50 and 60 grains. As an item of jewellery it was quite important and obviously at some time it had been lost, or sold, or perhaps even pledged against gaming debts. In its important setting and worn by a person normally associated with such fine jewellery, no suspicions as to authenticity would arise.

Thus, although natural pearl needs no flattery by imitation, in this latter description of the de Meisner imitation, the 'pearl' was flattered by the setting and the company.

A recent imitation pearl

A fairly recent imitation pearl has appeared upon the market. It has been described and illustrated by K. V. G. Scarratt, in 'Notes from the laboratory', in the *Journal of Gemmology*, Vol 9, 1984. This imitation pearl is marketed under the name of 'Angelo Pearls', and is advertised as follows: 'Only first-class shell material for the core is used and is identical to that implanted in oysters for the nucleus of the cultured pearl'. The descriptive wording conveys similarity to cultured pearl nuclei, this being the function of an imitation – to resemble the real thing as closely as possible. The Angelo imitation pearl has a mother-of-pearl bead nucleus which, as was described earlier in this chapter on the dangers of sophisticated tests, gives six-spot and four-spot lauegrams. The mother-of-pearl fluoresces and phosphoresces under X-ray excitation.

The Laboratory description states that the Angelo imitation pearls look a little livelier than other imitation pearls but, to the experienced eye, they did not 'look quite right'. The bead has three coatings of plastics-like material, the second one giving a discrete play of colour. As stated earlier, a first check procedure by the experienced gemmologist using a 10× lens would establish a man-made bead by examination at the drill hole. Here one would see the sharp finish of the cold grey mother-of-pearl bead surmounted by the softer and usualy ragged or torn appearance of the plastics or lacquer coatings. This ragged appearance at the drill hole is also seen in other cheaper glass-bead imitation pearls.

The 10× lens is an extremely simple and basic instrument which can be termed a 'low-power portable microscope'. Its constant use in preliminary examination of pearls and gemstones can furnish much information and can save time and materials from being wasted on advanced tests.

Chapter 9

The method of pricing pearls

In the pearl trade, pearls are bought and sold by weight, and historically their weight is expressed in grains. There are four grains to one metric carat. Thus, the pearl grain is a metric weight, 1 grain = 0.25 ct.

All other gemstone weights are expressed in metric carats, e.g. comparing a spherical drilled pearl weighing 10 grains with a ruby of equivalent weight the latter would be written as 2.50 carats.

Pearls are not priced at so much per grain but by an elaborate method using a base price referred to as the 'unit base price'. This unit used to be a one shilling base (1/-d) but is now 5p though the method remains the same. By a simple squaring of the weight of a pearl in grains and multiplying the result by the base (unit) price the value is arrived at. The pearl trade uses the phrase 'once-the-weight' which is the weight of the pearl squared which is once times its own weight. Often this phrase is abbreviated to 'the once'.

In the case of a pearl necklace the method is a little more complicated but only in simple arithmetical terms. As an example, take the actual trade tag attached to a necklace of 113 graduated pearls (*Figure 9.1*). The necklace is divided into eight groups of pearls, the central largest pearl is weighed by itself, the others are grouped together in 'sizes'. The number of pearls in each size group gives an indication of the steepness of the graduation of the necklace. In this particular case the two groups of pearls at the bottom of the list are the most numerous, i.e. 30 and 58 respectively, and are the smallest in average size, i.e. 2.40 grains and 1.35 grains respectively. It is visually obvious when the *average size* or weight of pearls is seen, that the graduation descends from the centre pearl 10.60 grains in fairly regular steps in round figures of 10, 8, 6, 5, 4, 3, 2 and 1 grain sizes.

If one pearl is dealt with on its own, it is simply a matter of multiplying its weight in grains by itself (once times) and then multiplying the result by the base value arrived at by the pearl merchant using the *unit base price* of 5p. The value of the centre pearl on its own would be at a one-unit base:

$10.60 \times 10.60 \times 5p = £5.61p$
At a valuation of a ten-unit base (50p) = £56.10p

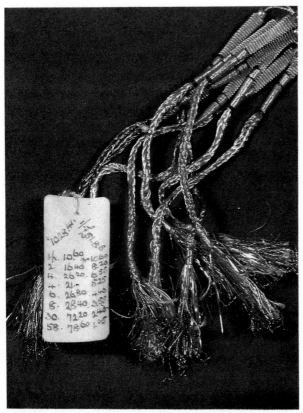

Figure 9.1 A pearl merchant's tag from a necklace of 113 pearls at 5p (base price) = £51.40. Silver tassels from Bombay supplies are also seen (Photo: A Jobbins)

The pearl necklace tag shows a brief pearl statement of 113 pearls, total weight 280.20 grains, with a once-the-weight of 1028.43 grains at the 5p (unit base price valuation) of £51.42p. This is a guide from which the merchant will calculate his trade price for the necklace. The pearl statement is obtained by taking the average weight of the pearls in each group and multiplying it by the total weight of the group. This is shown in broken-down form as follows:

Eight groups of pearls, of which the centre pearl is one group.

(a)   1 pearl weighing 10.60 grains average weight 10.60 grains
(b)   2 pearl weighing 16.40 grains average weight 8.20 grains
(c)   4 pearl weighing 26.20 grains average weight 6.55 grains
(d)   4 pearl weighing 21.00 grains average weight 5.25 grains
(e)   6 pearl weighing 26.80 grains average weight 4.46 grains
(f)   8 pearl weighing 28.40 grains average weight 3.55 grains
(g)   30 pearl weighing 72.20 grains average weight 2.40 grains
(h)   58 pearl weighing 78.60 grains average weight 1.35 grains

---

From the above calculations, which give the average weight of the pearls in each group, it is now possible to assess the total once-the-weight of the whole pearl necklace by totalling all of the groups together as follows:

Pearl statement

Pearls	Total weight	Once-the-weight	Unit base
1	10.60 grains	10.60 × 10.60 =	112.36
2	16.40 grains	16.40 × 8.20 =	134.48
4	26.20 grains	26.20 × 6.55 =	171.61
4	21.00 grains	21.00 × 5.25 =	110.25
6	26.80 grains	26.80 × 4.46 =	119.52
8	28.40 grains	28.40 × 3.55 =	100.82
30	72.20 grains	72.20 × 2.40 =	173.28
58	78.60 grains	78.60 × 1.35 =	106.11
113	280.20		1028.43

Thus, we now have the complete breakdown and analysis of the once-the-weight method which is particularly used for pearl necklaces, London and Paris being prime users of this method.

Anderson, in his 1983 revision of Webster's *Gems: Their Sources, Descriptions and Identification,* quotes (on p 519) from Richard Jeffries' (18th c) *A Treatise on Diamonds and Pearls* which said that the value of diamonds at that time was regulated by the square of the weight in carats, and that precisely the same process was laid down in the case of pearls.

The photograph of the pearl necklace tag is a condensed version which gives the pearl merchant concise details of the number of pearls and groups, their total weight and average weight, the total once-the-weight and the value of it at a 5p base.

The pearl *grain* weight is a metric weight and has *no* bearing on or relationship to troy weight (used for metal, gold, silver, etc) or avoirdupois (the old Imperial system for commodities such as sugar, sausages, potatoes, etc).

Whilst touching briefly upon the older system of weights and measures, it is an aspect of the international interest in pearls that natural pearls are weighed in grains but are reported on CIBJO certificates in carats. Cultured pearls are reckoned in millimetre sizes and sold by the momme (= 3.75 grammes) and in general the length of necklaces is expressed in inches.

The commercial advantage of 'sizing' pearl necklaces

Before the advent of radiography for determining pearl necklaces it was the practice to test every pearl of a necklace and to issue a certificate stating the number of pearls, their total weight and, of course, the result of the test. Some merchants would specifically ask for the pearls to be weighed in groups by size. In the pearl trade proper, necklaces of pearls would be sealed at each end, with a pearl tag attached giving the number of pearls in sizes and their weights, together with the value at the unit base price which started at 5p. These necklaces would be on single strands of silk, not knotted, and would be unclasped.

Observations upon the sizing of necklaces noted the commercial advantage of sizing a steeply-graduated pearl necklace compared to computation of its once-the-weight by taking only the average weight of the pearls of the necklace as a whole. With a necklace which had very little graduation there was not much to be gained by dividing the pearls into two main groups.

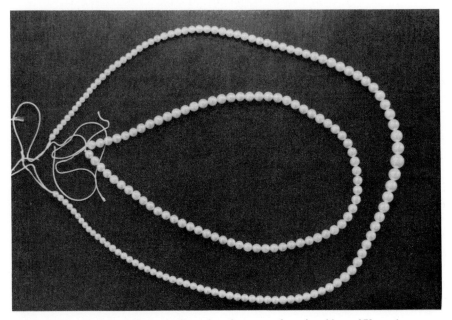

Figure 9.2 A graduated necklace of 117 pearls and a non-graduated necklace of 72 pearls (Photo: K V Scarratt)

An interesting example of the commercial advantage gained by sizing pearl necklaces in groups is given by the figures for the following two necklaces. Necklace A is steeply graduated, having a large centre pearl and small end pearls. Necklace B is very closely graduated, having practically only two sizes of pearls. Taking the average weight of the pearls in necklace A and multiplying it by the total weight gives a once-the-weight of 236.91 at unit base price 5p = £11.840. Taking the necklace in six groups of sizes, the once-the-weight is 418.12 at unit base price 5p = £20.90p. Necklace A shows considerable advantage gained by sizing. Taking the average weight of the pearls in necklace B and multiplying it by the total weight gives a once-the-weight of 476.58 at unit base price 5p = £23.82p. Taking the necklace in two groups of sizes the once-the-weight is 480.91 at unit base price 5p = £24.04p. Necklace B shows little advantage gained by sizing.

NECKLACE A

117 pearls   41.71 carats (166.84)
            average weight 1.42 grains   once = £11.84p

		average	*once*
1 pearl	8.44 grains	8.44	71.23
4 pearls	19.60 grains	4.90	96.04
10 pearls	32.80 grains	3.28	107.58
16 pearls	36.00 grains	2.25	81.00
30 pearls	34.96 grains	1.16	40.55
56 pearls	35.04 grains	0.62	21.72

418.12 at 5p = £20.90p

NECKLACE B

72 pearls   46.36 carats (185.44 grains)
            average weight 2.75 grains   once = £23.82p

	average	*once*
14 pearls 43.04 grains	3.07	132.13
58 pearls 142.36 grains	2.45	348.78

480.91 at 5p = £24.04p

Note that all pearl calculations are carried out to the second place of decimals only, the third figure is disregarded.

Chapter 10

A pearl pot-pourri

Those much-quoted lines from Gray's *Elegy*, 'Full many a gem of purest ray serene the dark unfathom'd caves of ocean bear', contain within them the accolade of purity which may well be an added attribute to the three required in the perfect gem. Beauty, rarity and durability are quoted as the touchstones or hall-marks of a perfect gem and throughout history pearls have commanded priority in terms of value and importance.

As gems they fulfil easily the requirements of beauty since they occur in nature and need no cutting, polishing or faceting as do all other gemstones. Rarity is yet another aspect achieved, usually by size, orient and symmetry. Durability is displayed in their tough physical structure of concentric overlapping layers of microscopically-fine radiating crystals of aragonite. This toughness is reflected in their ability to withstand pressure, and the resonance seen in their rhythmic bounce. Cultured pearls do not bounce in similar manner.

The symmetrical construction of pearls permits precise, accurate drilling, as opposed to that seen in radiographs of cultured pearls. When natural pearls are worked upon by a pearl broacher a smooth feel is experienced whereas a cultured pearl feels juddery and tends to snatch as the broacher turns.

Pearls are not usually subjected to bounce tests or hardness tests (although the author remembers occasions when every possible characteristic has been explored in efforts to decide the nature of a difficult pearl). The softness of pearls requires that they be handled carefully, worn carefully, regularly cleaned and examined, and not subjected to heat, acids, solvents or detergents. Thus it is necessary that all pearl necklaces should be regularly re-strung and knotted. A competent pearl stringer will, of course, wash them at that time in tepid Lux soapsuds. The string between the pearls is knotted to prevent their rubbing against each other and causing flat abrasions at the drill hole, also to prevent them from scattering should the necklace be broken whilst being worn.

Ridiculous statements have been made of pearls responding to a person's health, such as pearls looking lack-lustre when the wearer is ill or in poor health. From very close observations of thousands of individual pearls it is usually a case of pearls suffering from the wearer's acid skin, perspiration, spray from perfume, talcum powder or face powder and lack of regular washing and restringing of the pearls. In preparation for individual examination it is not unusual to find that the pearls adhere to each other in a continuous straight line after the silk thread has been drawn out of the necklace! This is not a natural affinity of pearls one to the other but a build-up of a cosmetic miasma acting as a soft gluey paste.

Some skins are more acid than others. If a pearl necklace is regularly worn, some of the pearls will constantly rest upon the neck at the shoulder line in close contact with the skin. Others occupying a more pendant position will not be subjected to such constant contact. The neck pearls, unless carefully checked, will gradually absorb acid from the skin; this will slowly eat into the spherical pearl and in time the pearl will not only look lack-lustre but will become barrel-shaped. A good pearl stringer will notice this and suggest replacements.

Pearls which have become barrel-shaped can sometimes be improved by the skills of a pearl doctor, although usually such skills are reserved for an important or potentially important pearl.

When pearls are not suitable to use in necklaces they can be used in other jewellery ornaments such as borders to brooches, festoons, or where the effect of more than one pearl, e.g. a cluster, is required.

Black pearls

At one time, if a cultured pearl was black, it was certainly stained artificially – usually by immersion in a solution of silver nitrate. The atomic weight of the silver in solution was much heavier than that of the calcium carbonate of pearl and thus, when radiographed, absorbed the rays to a much greater extent than the bulk of the pearl. Consequently, when the film was developed the result would show silver nitrate infiltration at the drill hole and in parts by concentric ring marking of faint white lines. These were termed 'reversals' because in a negative less exposure occurred via the reduced silver, giving a lighter effect like a white line, whereas the normal effect seen at conchiolin-rich demarcations would be heavy black areas, indicating the greater transparency offered to X-rays by conchiolin and thus greater exposure of the film.

Natural black pearls do occur, and some naturally-coloured black cultured pearls now emanate from Tahiti and possibly other places, due to the use of a black-lip pearl oyster. It has also been found that overlong exposure to X-rays will blacken some freshwater non-nucleated pearls. This is not so serious as possible blackening of natural pearls.

Natural black pearls have a faint reddish glow when viewed through crossed filters, i.e. when bathed in blue light from a copper sulphate solution and examined through a red filter. Artificially-stained black pearls do not have this red glow reaction.

Some Victorian jewellery had what looked like highly polished metallic black pearls set as ornaments. These often proved to be haematite, an iron oxide which, if rubbed on a streak plate (unglazed pottery will do), leaves a red streak. The red streak is literally a soft trace of powdered haematite – sometimes a constituent of rouge, sometimes used as a polishing agent.

See also section 'Imitation black pearls', page 125.

In an article 'The Black Pearl of Guyana', published in the *Journal of Gemmology* (Vol XV, 1976), J. G. Gosling describes black pearls found on the sloping banks of creeks in Aranka, Guyana (previously British Guiana). These 'pearls' are found embedded in a light, yellowish clay down to a depth of 14 in from the surface and they are obtained by washing and sieving.

They are said to be concretionary nodules of limonite; cross-sections show concentric banded structure of limonite around a clayey nucleous. These black pearls have an SG range of 2.64 to 3.52 and yield an orange yellow streak.

Photographs by Alan Jobbins accompany this article.

Lacquered mother-of-pearl beads

Although not of great importance, a danger encountered in laboratory testing was a lacquered (pearl-colour) mother-of-pearl bead. This bead gave a four-spot lauegram (cultured) pattern and exhibited a fluorescent and phosphorescent glow. To all intents and purposes it appeared to be a cultured pearl but examination with 10× lens showed the lacquered structure at the drill hole, and a less sophisticated test on the teeth gave a smooth feel, proving that a little practical knowledge in first application would have eliminated unnecessary and expensive tests. Sometimes erudite methods and sophisticated tests and equipment produce a situation where one cannot see the wood for the trees!

The radiograph of an *imitation* pearl necklace shown on page 116 is an example of a radiographer automatically X-raying a necklace without first examining it by use of lens as a first precaution.

Pearls in 'medicine'

When pearls reach the very nadir of their existence and become badly cracked and broken, then they are relegated to the drawer reserved for such tributes. At one time in Hatton Garden a dealer would call to buy these broken lots and remnants of seed pearl work for 'medical' purposes in the Far East. Gullible people thought they were useful as aphrodisiacs. When ground by pestle and mortar and stirred in distilled water the draught is beneficial in the same sense that 'indigestion' powders are – these contain a proportion of calcium carbonate which is the chief constituent of pearl. A sense of relief, if not well-being, extends from the digestive organs only.

Preservation

Pearls and cultured pearl are certainly susceptible to a variety of environmental hazards, among them being storage. Pearls should never be wrapped in cotton-wool because the heat generated would add to the drying out hazard; neither should they be washed in detergents, nor stored touching other jewellery for fear of abrasion from crystalline gemstones. Pearls, with care, can last for hundreds of years. If they are kept in very slightly damp linen – not in a coloured-velvet-lined case – this will off-set a dry atmosphere in a manner similar to humidifiers which assist in preventing the drying-out of fine furniture and panelling by central heating.

'Dying' pearls

There have been, and probably always will be, stories about pearls dying, but as one authority puts it, since they never lived, they cannot die.

One famous necklace known as the 'Thiers necklace' was owned by the wife of President Louis Thiers of France (1797–1887). The necklace comprises 145 magnificent pearls strung in three rows, the centre pearl of each row weighing 51, 39 and 36 grains respectively. This superb necklace was bequeathed to the Louvre Museum, Paris. During a period of its exhibition several letters were written stating that the pearls were 'dying'. This caused sufficient concern to prompt the director of the Louvre Museum to state in a written answer from Paris dated 26 June 1907: 'The necklace of Madame Thiers has caused much ink to flow, to such an extent that, a few months ago, the Minister ordered an examination to be made by three experts who have found that the pearls are in perfect condition and have never been in better health.'

Drilling and plugging

Natural pearls have much finer and straighter drill holes than cultured pearls, and their holes are smaller and finer because weight lost by drilling is money lost. Bombay is the home of the finest pearl drillers and X-ray photographs exhibit clearly the precise nature of their work. The minimum diameter agreed used to be 0.3 mm – this was the smallest diameter possible for endoscope needles.

When the drill holes are found to be too small, or even tight, broaching out of the drill holes becomes necessary. 'Broachers' are square-section needles of tempered steel tapering to a fine point, and they are held either in a small holder of with the fingers. Sensitive handling is necessary since they snap quite easily and, being tapered, become wedged in. On breaking a broacher in a drill hole, it helps to remember the direction of penetration. Some radiographs show these fine slivers of steel left in pearls, and new or opened-up drill holes are seen. These can be off-centre, necessitating plugging to obtain symmetry when threaded.

Various materials have been used as plugs. Chicken feather quills, plus wood (like fine 'Rawlplugs') are most popular; plaster-of-Paris and pearl cement are also used. Pearl cement is a thermoplastic, shellac-based, white material sold in paper-wrapped sticks resembling white sealing wax. It is used for fixing part-drilled pearls to studs, earrings and brooches, and can easily be unset by mild warmth and care.

Pearl fancies

Once of the most fanciful characteristics attributed to pearls is that of breeding or germination. At least two world authorities publish details of discussions and statements of pearls said to have increased in size and number after a period of time, after being enclosed with grains of rice. In neither case were absolute and undeniable controlled details available despite wordy affirmation of the honesty and reliability of the people concerned. In both cases where rice was included, the rice was found to be nibbled at the end of the period of germination. One authority had the grace, however, to admit that, despite the effect on the rice, the pearls remained the same in number and in size in *his* experiment. Doubtless if just rice were left under similar tropic conditions sealed in a box it would dry out and possibly present a nibbled appearance!

Other fanciful accounts of 'pearls' are reported from time to time in journals representing medical, mineral and geographical general interests. Unusual sources of 'pearls' range from coconuts to clouds, boars' heads, bamboo and elephants, among others. Dakin, in his book *Pearls,* says: 'It may be surprising to most readers of this little book to hear that pearl-like structures occur sometimes in plants. It may be quite incorrect to speak of them as 'pearls' but some of them, especially rare specimens from the coconut, are said to resemble in colour and appearance the real pearls from the sea.'

In a report in *Nature* for November 1947, and quoted in *Journal of Gemmology* of January 1948, Dr Reyne points out that coconut pearls claimed to have been found in a coconut are in fact true *Tridacna gigas* pearls, the chief component being aragonite. Deception is practised by local natives of the Celebes.

Cave pearls

Among other objects given not only the name 'pearl' but also an adjective prefix as well, are 'cave pearls'. These are termed 'pisolites', a type of limestone built of rounded bodies similar to ooliths, some 2 mm or more in diameter. They are formed by the accretion of concentric layers of calcium carbonate and a nucleus generally of a grain of sand or a small fragment of rock. Pisolites are common but are termed 'cave pearls' when they obtain a spherical or symmetrical rounded shape due to water action. Limestone caves in which regular dripping occurs produce cave pearls in a cavity where they are unattached – the water action gives them a high polish, almost a pearly lustre.

The present author, A. E. Farn, in the *Journal of Gemmology* (Vol XVII, 1981) gives an account and radiograph picture of cave pearls.

Royal purple

Among the many shells and shellfish of the huge family *mollusca* is a univalve gasteropod *Murex pupura haemestoma.* In early history the juice from the crushed shellfish was mixed with salt and boiled to produce a dye of reddish purple colour. The dye was termed 'Royal Purple' and was most expensive to produce as it took 300 lb of juice to dye 50 lb of cloth.

It was restricted to nobility, kings and emperors. 'To be born in the purple' comes from the history of a Byzantine emperor's son who was born in the porphyry room – a room of porphyry rock construction which was of purple crystals in a fine-grained ground mass. Disapproval was recently voiced by British Royalty over the use of purple vestments by the clergy.

Pearl fish and other intruders

Pearl fish are small eel-like creatures but are not eels. They are members of the *Carapidea* and are often found living inside *Holotharoidea* – the sea cucumber or bêche de mer. These minute creatures penetrate the pearl oyster and become trapped and eventually they are entombed, like flies in amber, by a coating of nacreous secretion. They are of considerable curio interest.

Dr A. E. Alexander, writing in the *National Jeweller* of December 1961, discusses irritants and intruders from his researches at the Mellon Institute of Industrial Research, Pittsburg, Pa, stated that although he had sectioned and thin-sectioned hundreds of natural pearls, very few had revealed any evidence of origin. Never did he find a 'grain of sand' but quotes finding a 'mud centre' in an American freshwater pearl. The pearl was ¼ inch in diameter, reddish in colour and weighed fractionally over one gram (5.08 grains). Analysis of the mud centre revealed clay particles, quartz grains, zircon and rutile.

More remarkable was the discovery of a rotifer in a 30-grain pearl which had been sectioned. (A rotifer is a microscopically small freshwater organism composed of a horny substance similar in composition to the finger nail.) Dr Alexander writing in 1939 in *The American Journal of Science,* said of the rotifer: 'It was so well preserved in its sarcophagus that is was possible to state sex and species. Named *Apsilus tentaculus,* it measured 0.375 mm in length by 0.140 mm in width. The funnel-shaped organism had fifteen spines, each 0.07 mm long'.

Dr Alexander stated that, 'the injection of such a spiny irritant would be enough to make any mussel quickly coat the intruder with liquid mother-of-pearl to soothe its unhappy interior. Being totally indigestible, its preservation was automatic!'

The pearl doctor

The pearl doctor is the cosmetic surgeon of the pearl world who improves pearls by delicately removing blemishes, his 'instruments' consisting of fine scrapers, abrasives and a sensitive touch, infinite patience and a considerable knowledge of pearls. In this aspect of the pearl trade, to simply describe the careful removal of a pimple or a blotch by use of miniature files or scraping devices would be accurate but not adequate.

'Doctoring' is a term which has hints of doping or interfering for some gainful purpose, not strictly honest or above board. Gemstone colours are often changed permanently by heat treatment, classic examples being heat treatment of greenish 'aquamarine' to an improved and more attractive blue. This is an accepted trade practice.

Pearls when first extracted from the tissue of oysters, particularly Japanese cultured pearls, are lightly bleached in a weak hydrogen peroxide solution. Sunlight also has a bleaching effect.

X-ray irradiation can cause darkening of colour in some pearls and is thus not a desirable effect, but generally speaking little 'doctoring' of pearls takes place to alter their colour. The causes of colour and choice of colour by precise inserts in non-nucleated cultured pearls is dealt with in the section 'Colour in pearls and cultured pearls', page 88.

However, an intriguing personality is conjured up when we speak of a pearl doctor! Two excellent books touch upon this aspect of the fascinating business world (see Recommended reading), one of which deals with pearls literally from the ground floor (or almost the ocean bed).

In the heyday of the pearl trade there were certainly pearl doctors in Hatton Garden, London, in the neighbourhood of Rue Lafayette, Paris, and in jewellery quarters of Maiden Lane, New York.

In some respects this working of pearls introduces the risk or gamble so beloved of many who deal in precious stones and pearls who put their hands in their pockets and take a calculated risk. It is usually only on large-sized and potentially valuable pearls that specialist skills are employed. No great risk or great financial loss is incurred with small and/or medium-quality pearls.

T. B. Elles, a native of Ceylon, was recognized in the boom days as being the most skilful of pearl doctors. He worked on pearls at Broome, Western Australia, and it was said that the Broome pearlers paid him quite handsomely to keep him in the town, presumably to work on blemished pearls, rather than go to London or Paris where he could have obtained employment in the jewellery world. T. B. Elles had a son, Charlie Elles, who was also in the pearl business at Broome but business there has dropped considerably. In Hatton Garden another father-and-son business of pearl doctors was Brockman & Son.

A pearler's tale

The exotic provenance of pearls from the warm waters of the East and Far East attracts the wealth of London, Paris and New York. Skilful, shrewd and knowledgeable dealers cater for this trade, and one of the most interesting pearl dealers who travelled widely, bought, sold and speculated, was Louis Kornitzer.

Born in Vienna in 1873 at the end of a long line of jewellers, Kornitzer was also gifted as a writer and fortunately for posterity wrote of his life and dealings to good effect. He wrote several books, among them *Pearls and Men*.

It is far more rewarding and interesting for the reader to find or borrow one of Kornitzer's books than to have long extracts copied out here. However, on the subject of superb pearl doctors and pearl dealers, one of the anecdotes is worthy of a summary, if only to whet the reader's appetite.

A Chinese owner of a ship-chandler's store on Chiro Pier, off Tulay, which juts a mile into the Sulu Sea, bought a quantity of opened shell. Whilst cleaning their exteriors he found on one of them a rounded attachment, greyish-black in colour, the size of a walnut. A fellow storekeeper offered him a bag of unhusked rice for it. Refusing, in true oriental fashion, the first offer, he later accepted 1½ bags of rice. In 24 hours it had changed hands several times and reached £100. Finally, a syndicate of Chinese traders bought it for £2000. It was decided that the blister, now separate from the shell, should be opened and that in the presence of the syndicate and potential buyers it should be worked by the best pearl doctor obtainable.

Just after breakfast, at least 30 Chinese who had a stake in the pearl, plus several European dealers, were assembled in the hot room as the doctor opened the first opaque cover to reveal a bright silvery patch, a pin's head in size. The blister was passed round for inspection and a small bid above £2000 was scorned. Ten minutes passed by. The doctor worked calmly and steadily, pausing only to wipe the sweat from his brow; it was 102° in the shade. The air was heavy with the breathing of the crowded spectators. The smells of Japanese 'whisky', Borneo tobacco burning in brass pipes, and odours of cooking combined to thicken the tension in the room. The pearl doctor longed for a drink but was denied alcohol, fearing for the value of the syndicate's goods. Bids were received as further work revealed a silver lining the size of a lentil. An hour later all the outer crust had been removed and the shape improved. £2500 was offered and refused. The pearl doctor worked on. By mid-day the piece had been reduced to a smooth-skinned oval of light silver grey, open in one place to show a silver white underskin. Great promise! £4000 was bid, still no acceptance. The pearl was passed round, the doctor was told to continue. The sun stood high, burning with equatorial fierceness. Tea, hot towels, whisky were passed round as the doctor worked through the siesta.

At three in the afternoon £5000 was bid and Tan Kim Tong, a wealthy dealer, offered to buy shares from syndicate-holders *pro rata;* three Chinese sold their shares.

At four o'clock the pearl was one-third of its original size, truly spherical, and the colour had changed to a peach rosée. The pearl looked worth £10 000. It was handed round and Kornitzer describes how he saw a circular indentation revealed which promised to continue throughout. He describes the pearl as ringed – no further treatment could remove it. No one would consent to stop and save face. Everyone present soon knew the truth.

At five o'clock the doctor wanted to stop but the syndicate insisted he worked on. Just short of nightfall seven-eighths of the pearl lay as a heap of white powder.

It was over, the Chinese host offered drinks all round and the Chinese members of the syndicate betrayed no outward signs of disappointment. The pearl doctor had provided a fair pearl at first which would have shown a reasonable return on the £2000. Sheer gambling had scraped away modest beauty to reveal a blemish which need never have been revealed.

The author has seen poor-quality, greyish-black, good-sized pearls which have shown regular structure by radiograph taken away from the laboratory and worked to a colour at least three shades better than was first seen. This is skilled pearl doctoring, a genuine improvement.

Famous pearls

Cleopatra's pearl

Cleopatra wore a magnificent pair of pearl earrings. At a feast she provided to impress Marc Antony with her wealth and/or love, she is said to have dissolved one of the pearls from her earrings in vinegar and drank it. This story, like the date 1066, is familiar to every school child. The value attributed to this pearl or pair of pearls was said to be 60m sestertii. It is difficult to work out in today's values how much money was involved. Kunz and Stevenson estimated the value in 1908 to be equal to 1 875 000 ounces of silver. Since it would be policy for court jewellers or valuers to wish to keep in favour, doubtless the figure suffers from inflation. The second pearl of the pair was cut in two to form ear pendants for the Venus in the temple of the Pantheon at Rome. The value of the second pearl which was bequeathed at the queen's death was given as 250 000 'escus' of gold. Again, difficulty is met in establishing proportionate value. These kinds of story grip public imagination and make useful ploys for novelists. What should be considered is the impossibility of dissolving a pearl in vinegar. A crushed pearl might slowly dissolve over a very lengthy period of time.

La Peregrina (the Incomparable)

La Peregrina is a pear-shaped pearl of 134 grains which was found at Panama in 1560. Streeter says that the shell in which it was found was thought too small to be worth opening. The Negro slave who found it was rewarded with his liberty, and his master with a plot of land and a local position of alcalde (Magistrate or Mayor) of Panama. Other authorities state that it came from Venezuela in 1574. It was presented to Philip II of Spain by a grandee named Dom Diego de Temes, and exhibited in Seville in 1597. It was given by Philip to Mary Tudor, 'Bloody Mary' and after her death was returned to Spain and graced the crown of the Blessed Virgin at Guadeloupe. It was worn in Madrid in 1605 by Queen Margarita of Spain to celebrate peace between England and Spain. Joseph Bonaparte, who abdicated the throne in 1813, passed the pearl to his niece Hortense de Beauharnais who in turn left it to Joseph's younger brother Louis Napoleon. In great need of money, he asked the Duke of Abercorn to sell it for him but the Duke bought it for his wife. She often temporarily lost it, due to its loose setting. It was temporarily lost at both Buckingham Palace and Windsor Castle. The Duke's son had La Peregrina drilled to make a secure setting for it. Its travels have recently been noted as at Parke-Bernet-Galleries, New York, 1972, (Elizabeth Strack, Perlenfibel, 1982, Rühle-Diebener-Verlag, Stuttgart, p 42).

Figure 10.1 Given by Louis XIV to Maria Mancini, niece of Cardinal Mazarin, the pearls in these ear-rings weigh over 400 grains the pair and were sold at Christie's NY for 230000 US dollars in 1979 (Photo: Christie's)

Figure 10.2 Drop-shaped natural pearls in the tiara of the Dowager Duchess of Marlborough, sold in 1979 for £36000 (Photo: Christie's)

La Pellegrina

It is unfortunate that another famous pearl should be named 'La Pellegrina', which can only cause confusion due to the similarity in both the sight and the sound of the words. However, La Pellegrina is perfectly spherical and weighs, according to Kunz and Stevenson, 111.5 grains, but Streeter gives it as about 90 grains. It is probably 111.5 grains since Kunz and Stevenson may have had more recent and accurate information. Both record it as having been purchased from an English admiral returning from India at Leghorn in Italy. It was purchased early in the 19th century, possibly 1818, by Z. P. Zozima of Zozima Brothers, Moscow. It has been variously described as the 'Moscow pearl' and the 'Zozima pearl'.

It is possible that it was originally part of the French Crown jewels stolen from the Garde-Meuble, Paris, in 1792. A pearl termed 'La Reine des Perles', weighing 27.5 carats (= 110 grains) was included in the stolen jewels. Zozima died in Moscow in 1827 and his collection is said to have been stolen by a compatriot. Records have it that a rich merchant who died in a convent in Moscow before 1840 had with him a superb spherical pearl in an elaborately-jewelled casket. In London in 1935 at an exhibition of Russian Art, a pearl was exhibited as 'La Pellegrina'. It was photographed by Arthur Tremayne, the original publisher and editor of *The Gemmologist*. Extremely well-annotated descriptions of famous pearls, necklaces and pearl ornaments can be found in Kunz and Stevenson's *The Book of the Pearl*.

Glossary of terms

Abalone   The name applied to the mollusc *Haliotis*. Sometimes termed 'ear shells'. They have a superior nacreous lining.

Adductor muscle   A muscle connecting the two valves of a bivalve and used for closing the shell.

Alveolar   Having pits over the surface and resembling a honeycomb.

Ama   Originally Japanese diving girls who fished for oysters – now a tourist attraction.

Aragonite   A major constituent of pearl. Rhombic-shaped crystals, SG 2.93.

Archipelago   A sea abounding in islands, a group of islands. Originally applied to the Mediterranean Sea which separates Greece from Asia (the Aegean Sea).

Auricle   A chamber of the heart connecting the afferent blood vessels with the ventricle.

Baroque   Any pearl of irregular form.

Bivalve mollusc   Species of shellfish having a pair of shells (valves), slightly hollow, with hinged ligament.

Biwa   The largest lake in Japan which has given its name to non-nucleated cultured pearls.

Byssus   The threads secreted by glands in the foot of certain shellfish, for attachment either to hard objects or to one another.

Carat   Metric weight = 1/5th gram = 4 pearl grains.

Cave pearls   An accretion of concentric layers of calcium carbonate around a nucleus, polished by water agitation in limestone caves.

Cephalopoda   The highest class of mollusc (exclusively marine) with four branchia, four kidneys and tentacles, e.g. squids, octopods and pearly nautilus.

Cercaria   Larval stage of many trematodes.

Cestode   A parasite flat worm consisting of a hooked head (scolex) and a segmented body (proglottides). The common tape worm is a cestode.

Conchiolin ($C_{32}H_{48}$)11).   An organic substance, a scleroprotein of keratin type, a substance akin to finger nails. The outer waterproof horny exterior of oyster shell (periostracum).

Conch pearls   Non-nacreous, usually pink, and ovoid in shape, from univalve *Strombas gigas;* termed 'Pink Pearls'.

Coq de perle   A blister-like hollow shell piece from the Indian nautilus, usually filled and backed.

Culch   The sea-bed area of suitable hard or rocky (coral) growth suitable for oysters to attach themselves.

Cyst pearls   True pearls from the tissues of shellfish in a pearl sac separate from the shell.

Doctor   Pearl doctor, a skilled technician, who with skill and care removes surface blemishes of pearls to improve them.

Endoscope   Apparatus used for optically viewing internal structure of pearls. Used only for drilled pearls.

Epithelial sac   A sac composed of epithelium, i.e. the pearl sac.

Epithilium   A layer of cells bounding a surface in the body of animals whether internal of external.

Essence d'orient   Originally fish scales from the bleak, a small fish from Seine, France, washed in spirit of ammonia, dissolved in alcohol and gelatine. Used on imitation glass beads to convey the effect of the 'orient' of natural pearl. Now manufactured from herring scales.

Fluorescence   Visible light exhibited by some materials when excited by irradiation of ultra-violet rays, X-rays, etc. If the luminescent effect continues after energy is discontinued, it is then termed 'phosphorescence'.

Freshwater pearls   Pearls from the freshwater shellfish *Margaritifera* (mussel pearls).

Gastropod, Gasteropod   A class of mollusca with distinct head, tentacles and eyes and flattened foot, e.g. the univalve *Haliotis* (abalone). On land it is a snail.

Gonad   Sexual gland of the oyster where nuclei are positioned for the production of cultured pearls.

Grain   A unit of weight for pearls. It is a quarter of a metric carat = 0.25 ct.

Haliotis   A genus of gastropod mollusc (univalve) termed 'abalone' or 'ear shell', sometimes 'ormer shell'.

Hinge pearls   Pearls of irregular elongated shapes found near the hinge of shellfish from fresh waters, sometimes termed 'dog tooth', sometimes 'wing pearl'.

Kan   A Japanese commercial weight = 1000 momme.

Keshi   A Japanese word for the smallest particle possible, e.g. a grain of sand, poppy seed. Slang for adventitious by-product of oysters seeded for culturing. Biwa non-nucleated cultured pearl is frequently termed 'keshi' – which it is not. The term 'keshi' is loosely applied to non-nucleated cultured pearls.

Littoral   The sea shore, land between high tide and low tide.

Lucidoscope   Apparatus used before the endoscope for viewing the zonal structure in some thin-skinned cultured pearls by means of an intense beam of light directed through an immersed cultured pearl.

Mabe   These pearls are purpose-grown cultured blisters which have their interior hemisphere nucleus of steatite removed and the hollow refilled and sealed; not to be confused with *Pteria penguin* pearls from Amami-Oshima referred to by the Japanese as 'Mabe pearls'.

Mantle   Two flaps arising, one on either side (right and left) of the body of the bivalve. Each flap has the same shape as the valve of the shell against which it always lies. Composed of connective tissue with an outer bounding layer of epithelium which is responsible for both shell and pearl formation.

Medicine   Term used for an injection into non-nucleated mussels to produce fancy shapes.

Medicine pearls   Usually seed pearls, dust pearls and broken remnants ground to powder and mixed with distilled water as a digestive aid. It has no aphrodisiacal properties.

Molluscs   A soft-bodied, non-segmented invertebrate animal which typically possesses a hard shell. The shell may be univalve as in snails, nautilus, etc, or bivalve as in oysters, cockles and mussels, and is sometimes reduced and internal as in cuttle-fish and slugs.

Momme   Japanese weight used for cultured pearls = 3.75 grams = 18.75 carats = 75 grains.

Muscle pearls   Small pearls found in the muscular tissue near its attachment to the shell.

Mytilus pearls   Pearls found in the common edible mussel *Mytilus edulis*.

Nacre   The mother-of-pearl layer secreted by certain molluscs and lining most bivalve shells. It consists of crystalline carbonate of lime, $CaCO_3$ with organic conchiolin and forms either all or only the outer layers of nacreous pearls.

Non-nucleated or **no-nucleus** cultured pearls   A slight contradiction in terms. A soft tissue insert as a nucleus into (originally) pearl mussels. The tissue disintegrates in time, leaving a void or no nucleus.

Nuclei   Several nucleus.

Nucleus   Usually a spherical bead of mother-of-pearl inserted into the soft body of an oyster to form cultured pearls.

Oriental pearl   Pearls from the true oysters genus *Pinctadine,* first applied to pearls from the Indian Seas.

Orient of pearl   The iridescent lustre reflected at the surface of a natural pearl, caused by reflection and refraction of light between thin films and at closely packed edges of layers.

Ostrea   The non-nacreous edible oyster.

Paar, par   The banks or shallows in Gulf of Mannar on which oysters live.

Periostracum   The horny exterior of mollusc shells secreted by the edge of the mantle.

Phosphorescence   The afterglow, continuing from fluorescence seen when certain materials are excited by irradiation of X-rays, etc.

Pinctada   The pearl-producing oyster, e.g. *Pinctada margaritifera, Pinctada maxima.*

Pinna pearls   From the Mediterranean Sea, lack-lustre and having a radiating structure of prismatic crystals rather than the concentric layered structure of oriental pearls.

Placuna   The window-pane oyster of Sri Lanka. The pearls have no great value; used chiefly for medicine.

Prismatic layer   The secondary layer of the mollusc shell, usually calcite prisms, which join the nacreous inner surface of mother-of-pearl (aragonite and conchiolin).

Sarcophagus   A limestone used by the Greeks for coffins; a stone coffin.

Sac pearls   Same as cyst pearls.

Seed pearls   Pearls of under ¼ grain in weight.

Spat   Very young oyster from one week old, 0.1 mm diameter.

Strombus gigas   The univalve conch shell from West Indies, Bahamas, which occasionally yields non-nacreous Pink Pearls.

Sumptuary laws   Laws passed in the Middle Ages restricting or prohibiting the use of certain objects, such as pearls, by the lower classes.

Trematode worm   A flat worm which is parasitic either externally or internally, as in 'liver fluke' in sheep. Another species causes pearl formation in the edible marine mussel.

Tridacna gigas   A huge bivalve clam sometimes attaining 500 lb in weight. Yields occasionally white non-nacreous pearls.

Unios   Freshwater mussels, sometimes termed 'clam' in America, preferring clear running streams with gravel/sand bottoms.

Recommended reading

Since this book treats its subjects very generally and is aimed at a broad spectrum of readers, not only gemmologists, retail jewellers and pearl merchants, but also interested sections of the general public, and is not intended to be used taxonomically, recommended reading can be less strictly channelled.

Many authors make considerable use of the great classic work *The Book of the Pearl* by Kunz and Stevenson which, since it has such a great spread of interest, can be read with pleasure by the non-specialist. A book which has very absorbing historical and archaeological interest is *The Book of Pearls* by Joan Younger Dickinson.

For narrative skill and shrewd insight, *Pearls and Men* by Louis Kornitzer is an absolute must. The 1950s book *The Pearl Seekers* is not a textbook but it has been carefully researched, and the author, Norman Bartlett, has written an extremely readable story about Australia's pearls and pearling life.

Each text page of *Pearls* by the Japanese writer Dr Shohei Shirai (who has several other books to his credit) appears in four languages, Japanese, English, French and Spanish. It combines technical and general interest for everyone, and is profusely illustrated with excellent colour photographs.

Gemstones for Everyman by B. W. Anderson does not deal solely with pearls; far from it, but the section on pearls has a style worth reading and reveals Anderson's personal knowledge of the trade and its characters. In contrast, one of the older books, *Pearls and Pearling Life* by Edwin Streeter, is written in an older style, Victorian certainly, but its authoritative manner and use of language make it a change from more sophisticated works. Edwin Streeter FRGS was well versed in navigation, not merely of pearling waters, but in those of commerce in London's Bond Street.

For those who wish to pursue the subject, full details of these recommended works, plus all those mentioned in the text and others, will be found in the References. In addition, though some books are out-of-print, Fellows and members of The Gemmological Association of Great Britain may be able to make use of that Association's library which contains a good selection of such books. Also, the Association's librarian can probably furnish names of members or Fellows who deal in gemmological works. The Association's address is St Dunstan's House, Carey Lane, London EC2V 8AB.

References

1 SHIRAI, DR SHOHEI, *Pearls*, Marine Planning Co, Wataraigun, Mie, Japan
2 POIROT, JEAN-PAUL (Paris Institut Nationale de Gemmologie) *Éléments de Gemmologie*, 1980
3 SPENCER, L. J., *A Key to Precious Stones*, Blackie, London, 1936 (p 230)
4 KUNZ, G. F. and STEVENSON, C. H., *The Book of the Pearl*, Macmillan, London, 1908 (opening)
5 DAKIN, W. J., *Pearls*, Cambridge UP, 1913 (pp 116, 4, 28, 123)
6 MARTYR, PETER, *De Orbo Novo*, 1517
7 HAWKINS, SIR RICHARD, *Voyage to the South Sea*, (1593), London, 1847 (p 133)
8 BENZONI, GIROLAMO, *Historia del Mondo Nuovo*, abr trans by Urbain Chauveton, Geneva, 1578
9 PLINY THE SECOND, *Historia Naturalia*, Bk **IX**, Ch 35
10 *The Travels of Pedro Teixeira*, Hakluyt Soc, 1608 (p 180)
11 RÉAUMUR, RÉNÉ, A. F. de, *Mémoires de l'Académie des Sciences*, 1717 (pp 177–194)
12 HOME, SIR EVERARD, *Philosophical Transactions*, Pt III, 1826 (pp 338–341)
13 FILIPPI, FILIPPO de, 'Sull origene delle perle', Il Cimento, *Revista di Scienze*, **Vol 1,** Torino, 1852 (pp 429–439)
14 GARNER, ROBERT, 'On the formation of British pearls and their possible improvement', *Jnl of the Linnean Soc*, Vol **XI,** 1873 (pp 426–428)
15 DUBOIS, RAPHAËL, *Comptes rendus de l'Académie des Sciences*, Vol **133,** 1901 (pp 603–605)
16 JAMESON, H. LYSTER, 'On the origin of pearls', *Proc. Zoological Soc.*, 1902, Vol **I,** (pp 140–166)
17 JAMESON, H. LYSTER, 'An examination of the cestode theory of pearl production', *Proc. Zoological Soc.*, 1912, (pp 260–358)
18 SPENCER, L. J., *A Key to Precious Stones*, 2nd edn, Blackie, Glasgow, 1946 (pp 229–231)
19 STREETER, EDWIN, W., *Pearls and Pearling Life*, George Bell & Sons, London, 1886 (pp 21, 254–259)
20 DICKINSON, JOAN YOUNGER, *The Book of Pearls*, Crown Publishers Inc, New York, 1968 (p 66)
21 ANDERSON, B. W., *Gemstones for Everyman*, Faber & Faber, London, 1976 (p 296)
22 REED, WILLIAM, *Huîtres Perlières de Polynesie*, Société des Océanistes, 1973 (pp 6, 27)
23 FARN, A. E., 'Back to the Persian Gulf', *The Retail Jeweller*
24 WEBSTER, R., *Gems: Their Sources, Descriptions and Identification*, rev by B. W. Anderson, Butterworth, London, 1983 (pp 525, 505, 519)
25 FIELD, D. S. M., 'Pearls of the seas and oceans', *The Canadian Gemmologist*, Vol **III,** No **4,** Autumn, 1982 (pp 7–13, 10)
26 The Australian Encyclopaedia
27 FARN, ALEXANDER E., 'Notes from the laboratory: Enjoying gemmology', *Jnl of Gemmology*, Vol **XVI,** No **6,** 1979 (pp 366–368)
28 ANDERSON, B. W., 'Notes from the laboratory, *Jnl of Gemmology*, Vol **XII,** 1971 (pp 206–208)
29 RUTLAND, E. H., 'The constituents of pearls', *Jnl of Gemmology*, Vol **XII,** 1971 (pp 219–225)
30 BOUTON, LOUIS, *Comptes rendus de l'Académie des Sciences*, Vol **CXXVII,** 1898 (pp 828–830)
31 BOSTWICK, LA PLACE, 'Growing pearls in the laboratory', *The Gemmologist*, Vol **V,** No **54,** 1936 (pp 143–145)
32 MACGOWAN, D. T., 'Pearls and pearl-making in China', *Jnl of the Soc of Arts*, Vol **II,** 1853 (pp 72–75)
33 OTSUTAKE, IWAZO, *Kokichi Mikimoto*, Japanese Tourist Office

34 TABURIAUX, JEAN, *La Perle et Ses Secretes*, Hammerle, Paris, 1983 (p 163)
35 GALIBOURG, J. and RYZIGER, F., 'Les méthodes d'examen et d'étude des perles fines et des perles de culture', *Revue d'Optique Théorique et Instrumentale*, Vol **6**, 1927 (pp 30–31)
36 ANDERSON, B. W., *Gem Testing*, 9th edn, Butterworth, London, 1980 (p 395)
37 SCARRATT, K. V. G., '*Notes from the laboratory*', *Jnl of Gemmology*, Vol **XIX**, No **2**, 1984 (pp 121–123)
38 JEFFRIES, RICHARD, *A Treatise on Diamonds*, 18th c
39 REYNE, *Nature*, Vol **CLX**, No **4071**, Nov 1947, quoted in *Jnl of Gemmology*, Vol I, Jan 1948
40 FARN, ALEXANDER, E., 'Notes from the laboratory', *Jnl of Gemmology*, Vol **XVII**, No **5**, 1981 (pp 287–288)
41 GOSLING, JAMES G., 'The Black Pearl of Guyana', *Jnl of Gemmology*, Vol **XV**, No **4**, 1976 (pp 209–211)
42 ALEXANDER, A. E., 'Freshwater cultured pearls. The history, methods and products of the cultured pearl industry', *National Jeweller*, Dec 1961
43 ALEXANDER, A. E., 'Pearl formation induced by a rotifer', *The American Jnl of Science*, **237**, 1939 (pp 920–922)
44 KORNITZER, LOUIS, *Pearls and Men*, 1935, also Penguin 541, 1946
45 STRACK, ELIZABETH, *Perlenfibel*, Rüle-Diebener Verlag, Stuttgart, 1982 (p 42)
46 BARTLETT, NORMAN, *The Pearl Seekers*, Andrew Melrose, 1954

See also

FARN, ALEXANDER E., 'Notes from the laboratory', *Jnl of Gemmology*, Vol **XV**, No **3**, 1976 (pp 123–125); Vol **XVI**, No **4**, 1978 (pp 223–235); Vol **XVII**, No **4**, 1980 (pp 223–229)
ANDERSON, B. W., 'The use of X-rays in the study of pearls', *Jnl of Radiography*, Vol **V**, No **49**, 1932; 'Pearls and cultured pearls' *Gemmological News*, (WJS & O), Nov 1938; 'Notes from the laboratory', *Jnl of Gemmology*, Vol **XII**, No **6**, 1971 (p 206)
WEBSTER, R., 'Unusual structures in pearls and cultured pearls', *Jnl of Gemmology*, Vol **IV**, No **8**, 1954 (pp 325–334); 'X-rays in the testing of gems', *Ilford X-ray Focus*, 1966 (pp 2–5)

Index